A NOVEL BASED ON THE LIFE OF
MARIA MONTESSORI

THE SOUL OF
A CHILD

Kate Fuglei

THE
MENTORIS
PROJECT

Barbera Foundation, Inc.
P.O. Box 1019
Temple City, CA 91780

Copyright © 2018 Barbera Foundation, Inc.
Cover photo: Pictorial Press Ltd / Alamy Stock Photo
Cover design: Suzanne Turpin

More information at www.mentorisproject.org

ISBN: 978-1-947431-15-7

Library of Congress Control Number: 2018949593

All net proceeds from the sale of this book will be donated to Barbera Foundation, Inc. whose mission is to support educational initiatives that foster an appreciation of history and culture to encourage and inspire young people to create a stronger future.

The Mentoris Project is a series of novels and biographies about the lives of great Italians and Italian-Americans: men and women who have changed history through their contributions as scientists, inventors, explorers, thinkers, and creators. The Barbera Foundation sponsors this series in the hope that, like a mentor, each book will inspire the reader to discover how she or he can make a positive contribution to society.

Contents

Foreword

First and foremost, Mentor was a person. We tend to think of the word *mentor* as a noun (a mentor) or a verb (to mentor), but there is a very human dimension embedded in the term. Mentor appears in Homer's *Odyssey* as the old friend entrusted to care for Odysseus's household and his son Telemachus during the Trojan War. When years pass and Telemachus sets out to search for his missing father, the goddess Athena assumes the form of Mentor to accompany him. The human being welcomes a human form for counsel. From its very origins, becoming a mentor is a transcendent act; it carries with it something of the holy.

The Barbera Foundation's Mentoris Project sets out on an Athena-like mission: We hope the books that form this series will be an inspiration to all those who are seekers, to those of the twenty-first century who are on their own odysseys, trying to find enduring principles that will guide them to a spiritual home. The stories that comprise the series are all deeply human. These books dramatize the lives of great Italians and Italian-Americans whose stories bridge the ancient and the modern, taking many forms, just as Athena did, but always holding up a light for those living today.

Whether in novel form or traditional biography, these

books plumb the individual characters of our heroes' journeys. The power of storytelling has always been to envelop the reader in a vivid and continuous dream, and to forge a link with the subject. Our goal is for that link to guide the reader home with a new inspiration.

What is a mentor? A guide, a moral compass, an inspiration. A friend who points you toward true north. We hope that the Mentoris Project will become that friend, and it will help us all transcend our daily lives with something that can only be called holy.

—Robert J. Barbera, President, Barbera Foundation
—Ken LaZebnik, Editor, The Mentoris Project

Chapter One

THE SOUL OF A PARENT

Maria Montessori lay with her head in her mother's lap. It was the end of August 1874, and Maria and her mother had spent the morning walking the hills of Chiaravalle looking for juniper berries. They had stopped to read from Antonio Stoppani's book *The Beautiful Country*.

Stoppani was Maria's great-uncle. Although Maria had yet to meet him, she felt she knew him from the stories her mother told.

"Your great-uncle is a philosopher priest, my darling," Renilde Stoppani Montessori was saying as she played with her daughter's dark curls. "His head is in the clouds, and he thinks about eternity. Yet his feet are on the ground, and he writes about nature. He writes about our country, so alive with natural beauty we all take for granted. His eyes are like yours, bright with curiosity. Someday you will meet him, and you will see. Tomorrow you will be four years old. He sent you this book for your birthday."

Both mother and daughter were tired after their long hike. They had walked to the top of the highest hill in Chiaravalle in Italy's province of Ancona. Renilde carried a basket covered with a red checkered cloth. In the basket were a bottle of water, a round of Parma cheese, three empty jam jars, bread she had baked that morning, and Stoppani's book. They passed a farmer who gave them a bunch of purple grapes from his vineyard. Afterward he watched them walk up the hill that overlooked the sea. He saw the thick book sticking out of the basket. Leaning on his shovel, he wondered why anyone would bring a book on a picnic.

Renilde had covered the ground with the cloth. She opened the book to read. "Don't fall asleep, my dear," she told Maria. "You may rest, but not sleep. Eternity will allow us plenty of time to sleep. I'll read to you from your uncle's book while you rest."

She began, "'The beauty of the country of Italy cannot be underestimated . . .'"

As Maria took in the words, she looked out over the Ancona harbor. She saw old women dressed in black walking near the ancient fountain in the plaza. From Maria's perspective, they looked like ants. She saw ships bobbing in the harbor. She imagined smartly dressed ships' captains supervising the loading and unloading of carts filled with dried tobacco leaves and goatskins.

Maria's father, Alessandro Montessori, was in charge of tobacco sales for the government. He was a proud civil servant. Maria and her father often took long inspection walks in the tobacco fields that spread out for miles around Chiaravalle.

Now her eyes focused on the three jam jars that sat on ground in front of her. Inside them were the real objects of the mother-and-daughter hike. Renilde and Maria had found three chrysalises and put them in the jars with juniper berries, twigs, and leaves.

The night before, at dinner, Maria had asked her mother, "What is a chrysalis?"

"A chrysalis is a shell a caterpillar makes around himself. He creates this shell as a way to protect himself while he grows the eyes, legs, and antennae he needs to become a butterfly. He does this by eating a protein soup—"

"Please!" Alessandro interrupted. "Let me eat my soup in peace! What kind of dinner discussion is this for a four-year-old girl?"

"Alessandro, our daughter asked me a question. I am merely answering it."

"I would like to change the subject to something more pleasant," he replied sternly.

"But Papà, we are going for a hike tomorrow to find caterpillars!" Maria protested.

"I said enough. We won't discuss whether hunting for caterpillars is a suitable activity for a little girl." Alessandro looked pointedly at his wife. Maria turned to her mother, who put a finger to her lips.

Renilde began to eat her soup. Maria did the same. Later, as Renilde and Maria said their goodnight prayers, Renilde told her daughter, "All things alive, including the caterpillar, must be protected so they can grow. When they are protected, each part of the caterpillar can find its potential."

"What is *potential*, Mamma?" asked Maria, leaning her head on her mother's shoulder.

"The best that we can be. Good night. May the Lord bless

you and keep you safe. May the Lord look after all children, especially those who are poor and in harm's way."

On the hilltop, in the warmth of the afternoon, Maria considered the word "potential" and stared at the three jam jars. As she rested on her mother's lap, she wondered what her father would make of the caterpillars. Suddenly she saw a tiny movement, a cracking of the chrysalis. The sun touched the horizon of the Adriatic Sea. Her mother closed the book and began gathering the jars and their picnic. It was time to walk down the hill to their stone house in Chiaravalle.

Alessandro would be home in an hour. He would be hungry and ready for an early dinner. Tonight was the monthly meeting of his military colleagues. They had all fought with Garibaldi to free Italy from Austrian control. The gathering included officers and enlisted men. As Alessandro often told his wife and daughter, "We all fought equally for the glory of Italy. Loyalty has no rank."

There were fifteen of the veterans, and they all lived in or near Ancona. The Montessori house was the most convenient place to meet. And Alessandro had been their commander.

"What exactly is the purpose of these meetings?" Renilde had asked more than once. She didn't look forward to the muddy boots and cigar smoke. "Besides loud stories, drinking, and card playing?"

"These men are my family, my brothers in arms," Alessandro always protested, "You owe them eternal gratitude. They unified our great country. I am honored to have them in my house and you should be, too. We meet to remember, to commemorate, to never forget the sacrifice, to always be prepared."

"I think you meet to tell old war stories and drink wine," said Renilde, chuckling.

"We are soldiers," answered Alessandro, shrugging. "That is what we do."

Maria and Renilde arrived home as darkness fell. They immediately went to work. Maria didn't need to be asked. Her mother had taught her to be of assistance. The Montessoris had no household help; Renilde didn't believe in it. "Why should we pay someone to do what we can do ourselves?" she said.

Maria pulled a stool to the cupboard and brought down plates and bowls. She placed them on the table. Renilde lit the stove. Maria carried a pot of ribollita, a soup made of white beans and pancetta, to the stove. Soon it was simmering and filling the house with the smell of basil and thyme. Meanwhile, Renilde laid out her husband's red shirt on a chair. He wore it to all the meetings in honor of Giuseppe Garibaldi, the great Italian general and a father of the fatherland.

Alessandro burst into the room excitedly, as he always did on meeting nights. He picked up his daughter, who was waiting for him by the door. "And what the devil are these?" he said as he sat down at the table. He pointed to the jam jars. "Don't tell me we are having leaves and worms for dinner."

"No, Papà," said Maria. "They are caterpillars. And they will soon be beautiful butterflies!"

"Please put them away from the dinner table and let us say our prayers and eat. My men will be here soon."

Maria carefully carried the jars to the butcher block next to the sink. The Montessori family said grace and ate quickly. After dinner, once the table was cleared and the dishes were put away, Maria and Renilde went upstairs to a small bedroom, where they sat knitting. They did this every evening. They gave what they made to the poor.

Soon the small house was filled with the sound of boisterous voices and the smell of tobacco. The slap of cards on the table and the pop of corks being pulled from bottles signaled it was time for Maria to go to bed. Renilde opened the door of the room where they had been knitting. Voices wafted up.

Alessandro had taught the men the card game Trappola. Having quickly dispatched the minutes of the meeting, the men got down to the game. Maria sneaked downstairs and stood behind her father, glancing at his hand.

"Say aces, Papà. Aces!" she said excitedly at one point. Absorbed in their hands, the men had not noticed her presence. Her father winked at his friends, as if to say he was indulging his little girl. He followed her whispered advice for a few hands. It was always right.

"That little mite can't really understand the game, can she?" asked Roberto, one of the former enlisted men.

"She seems to be beating the hell out of you!" said Emilio, taking a swig from a silver flask.

Roberto bristled. "Alessandro, it's time for prayers and the sandman for your little card shark."

Maria reluctantly began walking up the stairs. Then she turned around. "Papà has already won," she said in a clear, steady voice. "He has accumulated three hundred points. Count them yourself." The astounded players did just that. Maria was absolutely correct. She sat on the top step, watching as they played and listening to their war stories.

Roberto was saying, "'As Hunters of the Alps,' I said to this Austrian priss, 'Catafalmi is ours!' I heard Garibaldi himself say,

'Here we either make Italy or we die!'" Roberto made a sweeping gesture, as if he were wielding a saber. The jam jars that held the caterpillars fell to the floor and shattered. Stepping back in inebriated confusion, Roberto smashed two of the chrysalises under the heel of his boot.

Maria raced down the stairs. She stood in front of Roberto, glaring up at him, a tiny creature in a white nightgown facing down a giant in a red Garibaldi shirt. "You've killed my caterpillars. You've smashed them. You've broken their homes."

The drunken ex-soldiers were shocked into silence. Then Roberto said sheepishly, "Little Maria, what's the fuss?"

Maria looked at him coldly. "You have murdered my caterpillars."

Alessandro called upstairs sharply, "Renilde! Where are you? Get this child to bed, for God's sake." He glared at Maria. "Apologize immediately. No child talks to an adult that way in my house."

"It's late," said Roberto. "We should all be getting home." It was not late, and the card-playing and camaraderie usually went on for many more hours. But the joviality had left the room. The men bid a hasty goodnight.

Maria went to her room and lay on her bed. She could hear the sound of glass being swept up. Her window was open, and as Roberto left the house, she heard him say, "We stood up to Garibaldi. But I wouldn't want to face that little mite on the battlefield." As the crunching of their boots faded away, Maria heard voices in the kitchen below.

"She should be playing with dolls, not collecting worms," said Alessandro. "You are spoiling her."

"They are caterpillars, not worms," Renilde answered, speaking calmly. "It isn't spoiling to encourage her mind, her curiosity, her intellect. Alessandro, she is reading at the age of four. She understands what she reads. She is already doing complicated math. You saw her at the card table tonight."

"It doesn't give her the right to be disrespectful to adults. I won't have it!"

Maria climbed out of bed and walked down the stairs to the kitchen. Her parents were face-to-face in a tense standoff. Maria dragged a chair between them, climbed onto it, and took her mother's hand. She placed it in the palm of her father's hand and closed his fingers around it. Maria's dark eyes met the eyes of her parents. There was a long moment of silence. Alessandro smiled in spite of himself. He took a long look at his daughter and said, "We'll never get up for Mass tomorrow if we don't all get to bed."

The quarrel was over.

Mother and daughter took special care to dress beautifully for Sunday Mass the next day. It was Maria's fourth birthday. They knew Alessandro took pride in the appearance of his family. It was important to him to present a picture of rectitude and pro-priety. Renilde brushed her daughter's dark curls into a mass at the nape of her neck. She tied them with a yellow grosgrain rib-bon.

Maria and Renilde wore matching white crinoline dresses. Alessandro was dressed in his military summer whites. As they walked the six blocks to the service, their neighbors commented on what a handsome trio the Montessori family made.

After the Sunday service, Alessandro proposed a surprise trip to Loreto, a small town by the sea that had a famous chapel. Perhaps it was a way to make up to his wife and daughter for the night before. Or maybe it was a birthday treat for Maria. Either way, they happily agreed. They boarded the train in the small brick station at Chiaravalle.

As the train sped around the bay, Alessandro told Maria the story of the Greeks who brought purple dye to Ancona. Then Renilde told the story of how angels, fearing for the safety of the Virgin Mary's home in Nazareth, had flown the sacred house to the safety of Loreto. Around it, a beautiful basilica had grown.

"Actually, it was brought by boat to save it from marauding Saracens," said Alessandro as the train sped by the sparkling Adriatic.

"Why must you always contradict me?" asked Renilde.

"In any case, it is a holy site. It was saved. And we will see it!" said Maria, already familiar with the ways to smooth over family quarrels. Her heart was pounding with excitement. She didn't want anything to ruin the day.

"It is where redemption began," said Renilde. "It is one of the most important and sacred places possible. It is where Mary came to know she would be the mother of our Savior. It is the true heart of Christianity—the house where Mary was educated, where she received the Annunciation, where the angel Gabriel appeared."

The train chugged up the final hill to Loreto. As the town came into sight, the Montessoris sighed with pleasure. They could see the top of the Basilica della Santa Casa. It was surrounded by green rolling hills.

A hush fell over the family as they made their way toward the white marble outer walls. Inside, in a low voice, Renilde pointed out the cupola, the treasury room, and the angels painted on the ceiling.

As they stood before the small three-sided room inside the basilica that had been Mary's home, tears came to Maria's eyes.

A painting of the Virgin Mary holding her child, the baby Jesus, was full of such tenderness it seemed to Maria to be the essence of love. "Mamma, see how she is holding her child," she said to Renilde. "From protection, love can grow."

The family was quiet as they made their way back to the train station at Loreto. The trip to the shrine of the Holy House had felt like a benediction. "Mary said yes to God there," Renilde reminded them. "And we must ask ourselves, what do we say yes to? What is our purpose in life, the reason we were put here, the mission God has given us?"

The sun had almost set as the train made its way into the harbor below Chiaravalle. Alessandro cleared his throat and said, "This is as good a time as any to tell you that I have been transferred to Florence. The department of finance has determined that is where I can best serve. Maria can begin her schooling in a more sophisticated atmosphere than the school at Chiaravalle."

Renilde didn't speak. She leaned her head against the horsehair seat of the train. She stared at the last rays of the sun across the water in the harbor. She held her daughter's hand and decided the move would be good for Maria.

That night, as Maria and Renilde knelt to say their prayers, Maria felt something cold against her knee. She lifted the bed skirt and saw a jam jar. Inside, a contented caterpillar was clinging to a stick.

"I found him in the garden this morning," said Renilde.

"Can I take him to Florence?" Maria asked. "So he can grow into a butterfly?"

Renilde nodded. "With enough love and protection, all creatures can find their potential."

∾

A month later, the Montessoris moved to Florence. The beauty of the city appealed to Renilde and four-year-old Maria. The soaring architecture beckoned them to long walks through the winding streets, crossing the Arno on the Ponte Vecchio.

The streets of Florence, while filled with prosperous business people and political leaders, also teemed with the less prosperous and the forgotten. There were no beggars in Chiaravalle, and Maria had never before been confronted with the plight of the poor.

Mother and daughter walked all over Florence, from Piazzale Michelangelo to the Basilica of Santa Croce. Each day, they encountered the open-air museum of some of humankind's greatest architectural and artistic accomplishments. They also saw, in the faces of the destitute, some of the lowliest and most needy. Renilde did not shield her daughter from these sights. The children in particular tugged at Maria's heart.

As their first days in Florence sped by, Maria kept close watch on her caterpillar. It began to shed its cocoon. As the skin around the caterpillar became more translucent, Renilde and Maria could see the orange-and-brown wing markings of a butterfly.

One morning, Renilde announced, "Today we will make our first visit to the Santa Maria del Fiore. We will climb Giotto's bell tower and release our butterfly." It was a hot day at the end of September. Alessandro wanted to stay home but was talked into the excursion by his wife and daughter.

They had seen the outside of the Florence cathedral, but nothing prepared them for the beauty of the interior. Maria carefully held her jar while they climbed the 414 steps of the campanile. Renilde and Alessandro stopped frequently on the claustrophobic stairwell to wipe their faces. Maria kept a slow and steady pace.

They were rewarded at the top with a stunning view of Florence. They could see the massive dome designed and built by Brunelleschi. They could see the red-tiled roofs stretching out over the city, and the mountains beyond.

As her parents caught their breath, Maria looked at her jar. A butterfly had emerged. Its wings were beginning to move. She removed the lid and held up the jar. Seeing the beautiful creature climb to the lip of the jar, she whispered, "All things, when protected, can reach their potential."

The butterfly moved its wings slowly in place. Its wings began to flutter. It hovered briefly in mid-air just above Maria's head. Then it flew into the blue sky above Florence.

Five months later, Alessandro strode into the vestibule of their second-story Florentine apartment. He was beaming. It was late February 1875. The chill of early evening was lessened by the smell of ciambotta, a vegetable stew that Maria had prepared all by herself.

Maria ran to him to show him a small book she had finished. "It shows how to make five different meals, with measurements and pictures I drew myself!" It was bound with thin ribbons.

"What will you do when you start school?" her father asked with a laugh. "You will be teaching the teachers! I am sorry I am late. But I stopped off at the Café Gilli to celebrate."

"Celebrate what?" asked Renilde.

"I have been promoted again," he said proudly. "I still think you will be teaching the teachers, little Miss Maria. But you will be doing it in Rome. That is where we will move in the summer."

Chapter Two

THE SOUL OF CHILDHOOD

When the Montessoris arrived in Rome in August 1875, the city was in the midst of Risorgimento fever. The unification of Italy was nowhere more visible. Rome had always been a center of learning, culture, and power. It was now the capital of a newly unified country. Victor Emmanuel II was king, and Italy was poised for rebirth.

The growth of Rome attracted a massive cadre of workers to build new housing. Liberal reforms were undertaken, and Alessandro Montessori was the beneficiary of an expanding government bureaucracy. Rome was determined to bring Italy into the modern age.

Not all reforms were equal, however. Education lagged behind. Primary and elementary education were left to the quirks of individual communes. Teachers were poorly paid. Schoolrooms were dirty. Administrators were fired or changed at the whim of local politicians. Schools had few curriculum standards and no unified philosophy of education.

Urban schools and their students fared better than rural. The school systems in Northern Italy were, for the most part, more progressive than those in the south. But in general, all schools in Italy at the time were woefully inadequate. The illiteracy rate, especially among Southern Italians, was staggering. The vast majority of children did not attend school after third grade.

Almost all public elementary schools followed the John Lockean principle that the mind of a child is an empty vessel into which adults must pour reason and knowledge. John Locke was a seventeenth-century English philosopher whose ideas about education had a profound effect on Western European thinking. His notion of the child's mind as a tabula rasa, or blank slate, provided a guiding principle for educational methodologies: if the young child's mind was a blank slate, the teacher's job was to fill it.

Maria Montessori was six years old when she began her education at the public school on the Via di San Nicola da Tolentino. Located in a middle-class section of Rome, it was better than most.

The outside of the building was gray stone. Inside were two floors with brown walls, worn terra-cotta floors, and rooms in which writing tables were attached to wooden benches. There were few books and no pictures or paintings. A large blackboard stood at the front of every classroom. A glowering teacher stood before the blackboard. This was the dismal setting where Maria and thirty-nine other six-year-olds found themselves.

Some children had hornbooks. A hornbook looked like a wooden paddle and was covered with a thin sheet of transparent mica. The alphabet was painted on the paddle. The vowels and consonants were written on the first sheet of mica. The Trinitarian formula, "The Father, Son, and Holy Ghost," was also written on the sheet, along with the Lord's Prayer and Roman numerals.

The children sat quietly. Their hornbooks dangled by strings from their chairs. Not all the children had hornbooks, so those who did shared with their classmates. The morning was long. The teacher, a wizened woman with skin like a dried apple, droned on and on about the first three letters of the alphabet. The students were called to the board one by one to repeat and write the letter A.

It was boring. Maria thought about her Uncle Stoppani's book. She copied the letter when it was her turn, but did so with a lackluster energy, like the other children. Whatever excitement they brought to the first day drained away.

At twelve o'clock, the children were let out into a small, crowded courtyard with their lunch pails. There were no swing sets, balls, or baskets. There was nowhere to sit. The small square of stone baked under the noonday sun. A hazelnut tree provided the only shade. The ground was covered with dropped hazelnuts.

The children clustered under the shade of the hazelnut tree. They sat listlessly after finishing their lunches of buttered bread and pancetta.

Maria had an idea. "Let's play Fazzoletto Peo Peo using hazelnuts!"

Rafaella, a small blond girl with long braids, yawned and said, "How do you play it?"

"We all sit in a circle, and one person who is It walks around the circle and drops a hazelnut behind someone. That person jumps up, runs in the opposite direction, and the winner is who-ever gets back to the empty space first."

The children, except for Rafaella, jumped up to make a

circle, chattering with excitement. They listened with attention to Maria's quiet but assured directions, and the game began. Squeals of laughter filled the yard as the children cheered, ran, and clapped.

Rafaella stood aside, watching. She was jealous of the success of Maria's suggestion. After a few rounds, she stepped into the circle and said, "Let's drop lots of hazelnuts so lots of children are running in different directions all at once."

Maria went to stand beside Rafaella. "That idea is neither safe nor logical," she said. "Someone will get hurt."

None of the children knew what the word logical meant. But they were persuaded by Maria's calm and authoritative manner. They ignored Rafaella. She stamped her foot in anger and walked back into the schoolroom.

From that moment on, Rafaella was Maria's challenger and competitor. Maria mostly ignored her. She had no interest in competition for competition's sake.

Near the end of Maria's fifth year in school, the teacher announced contests in spelling and mathematics. There would be prizes for the best students. She encouraged the students to sign up.

Rafaella's name was first on the list. Maria didn't bother signing up. She did well enough in school. But her true joy came at the end of the day, when she was released to the loving arms of her mother.

Maria rarely mentioned the events of the day at school. They were too boring. Instead, she spoke about the things she and Renilde saw on their walk home: the flowers and trees, the mass of Roman humanity they passed along the way.

Maria noticed every detail. One neighborhood girl had

a physical deformity. She was a hunchback. She didn't attend school. Maria spoke with her often and befriended her.

When the contests took place, Rafaella won the blue ribbons. Her parents, who were friends of the Montessori family, bragged about their daughter's prowess. Alessandro was livid and later complained to his wife.

"Maria was reading at the age of four! She could add, divide, and do complicated math! I know that for a fact. I made a killing at card games because of her. Why did she not compete? Why is she spending her time with hunchbacks? Why isn't she doing normal things?"

"I don't know, Alessandro!" Renilde Montessori said. "Perhaps you should ask her yourself."

From her bedroom on the second floor of their apartment, Maria could hear her parents argue. She walked slowly down the marble stairs, worn by generations of occupants. She came to the bottom step and faced her father.

"Papà, competing for a ribbon has nothing to do with learning. I love learning. But ribbons don't matter to me because I teach myself. Regina, the girl with the hunchback, has taught me so much. She has a bright mind. I am learning about her by seeing how she learns."

Renilde looked down, avoiding her husband's eyes. He was a proud man. Maria understand this as well. She looked down at the floor. They waited. Finally, Alessandro sighed.

"As a soldier who risked his own life, and those of his men, to unify this country, I know it is not enough to fight," he said sternly. "One must win! Not for self-glory, but for the greater glory of our country. Never forget, in all that you do, you are representing the proud Italian empire. It is not enough to learn. You must lead! Accept challenge. Go right to the heart of it.

Don't ever back down or back away. Do you understand what I am saying? Never forget this."

Maria put her small hand into her father's large, battle-scarred hand.

"I will never forget, Papà," she said, meeting his eyes, "I will be a leader. For the glory of Italy."

Maria did what she could to keep her promise to her father. During her elementary years, she was an outspoken and undisputed leader, in particular on the playground. She was never shy about voicing her opinions, popular or not.

Some of her peers called her bossy. Maria often smiled at this, saying, "In my opinion, you aren't even born yet." Whether or not they agreed with her, the other students listened to her. Maria's determination and authority blossomed.

When she was ten years old, Maria contracted a serious case of pneumonia. Renilde sat by her daughter's side day and night. After nearly a week of high fever, Maria opened her eyes and said, "Don't worry, Mamma. I won't die. I have too many important things to do."

As Maria approached womanhood, Renilde marveled at her daughter's self-possession. She encouraged it. Her father was less enamored of his daughter's forthrightness, but he took great pride in her beauty and intelligence.

In late May 1882, nearly twelve-year-old Maria was walking down the steps of her elementary school when she saw Renilde running toward her. Her mother was waving a piece of paper. She looked breathless and excited. She enveloped her daughter in a strong hug. "Uncle Stoppani is coming here to Rome! He will stay with us!"

During the next week, the entire Montessori family prepared for the visit. Antonio Stoppani, priest, geologist, paleontologist, scholar, and author, was coming to Rome to see his niece and grand-niece, as well as to visit the Vatican and the Pope.

Maria and Renilde cooked and cleaned. They made the family specialties: brasato, a stew of beef marinated in wine; potato gnocchi; and the sweet corn tarts, cobeletti. They reread several of Stoppani's books and displayed them prominently on the mahogany table in the front hall.

Finally the day came. Alessandro, Renilde, and Maria made their way to the train station. The train arrived with a puff of steam, and Antonio Stoppani alighted. He stood out immediately in his brown wool cape. He embraced Renilde warmly. He knelt down to Maria and looked into her eyes. He smelled of lemon verbena.

Maria was enchanted. It was as though no one existed but the two of them.

"I have read every one of the letters you have sent me over the years, my dear," Stoppani said. "You have a keen mind. I cannot wait to talk with you about volcanic eruptions, the history of Rome, and the dawn of a new age. We are on the verge of a great leap for humanity. We will rely on brilliant young minds like yours. You are the hope of the future."

Maria's eyes shone. No one but her mother ever spoke to her like this, like an equal.

On the way to the apartment, Maria and Stoppani sat in the back of the carriage, deep in conversation. Alessandro and Renilde sat in front.

Alessandro whispered to his wife, "This can't continue. The child is already taking up too much of his time. It is unseemly."

Renilde smiled and said nothing. She knew Stoppani would do just as he pleased.

The week was jolly, full of animated discussions on many topics: nature, religion, philosophy. Maria participated in all the conversations. Because Stoppani treated her as an equal, it would have been rude for Alessandro to correct her. She spoke freely during their dinners, a behavior Alessandro would never allow under normal circumstances. Stoppani encouraged her with playful and sometimes pointed conjectures.

One evening, while they were discussing the Risorgimento, Stoppani voiced his opposition to some of its nationalistic aspects. "While I wholeheartedly support it, I feel we have much to learn from other countries. I fear becoming too myopic."

Maria said, "I have been thinking that too much national pride can mean we don't listen to other countries, from the lessons they have learned. Isn't it better to have a more worldly perspective?"

Alessandro, a dedicated civil servant and proud Italian who had fought for unity, had enough. It was to him unthinkable for anyone to call into question the notion of nationalism, whether it was an esteemed relative or his own daughter.

"I won't hear that in my house. Maria," he said sternly. "It is time for you to go to bed. I, too, am retiring. Goodnight, Father Antonio."

Perhaps it was a salve for the previous evening. Or perhaps he had planned it all along. But the next day, Stoppani took Maria to the Vatican.

She had seen it before, but always from the back of a large holiday crowd. This time, with her uncle, she passed along corridors that grew smaller and more intimate as they walked.

She held her breath as a phalanx of priests, all of whom seemed to know Stoppani, opened a small white door.

The red carpet glowed in the midday sun. Light poured through a stained-glass window and fell across the face of Pope Leo XIII. Maria kissed his hand and looked into his eyes.

"This young woman is going to do great things," said her proud uncle.

"What is your name, my child?" the Pope asked.

"My name is Maria," she answered.

"Ahhh. There is no name more sacred. Children are our hope, the future, and the greatest of God's blessings. You must be protected until you can know God's purpose for you. That is the greatest part of life: to know our purpose and to fulfill it. Let no one deter you. May God show you mercy all your days, and may His spirit of peace shine through you."

He put his hand on Maria's head, blessing her. Once more, she looked into his eyes. They were like two warm brown pools reflecting soft light.

Maria floated on air as they left the Vatican. She was, for once, speechless as they rode home. They passed elegant Romans making their way on the Via della Conciliazione. They passed through the San Lorenzo district, where Maria saw thin, dirty children begging on the streets. Several picked through the garbage outside a shop until the owner shooed them away.

Maria marveled that the same day could encompass a meeting with the Pope and the sight of the city's most desperate and destitute. She saw there was immense suffering in the world. She turned to Stoppani and said, "I want to go to engineering school. I want to be an engineer. I want to help build a better world, houses for the poor. I want to physically make things that can help people who need them. I want to continue my education in *liceo*. Not many women go. Papà won't like it."

"No, my child, he won't," Stoppani agreed. "But if you believe this is your purpose in life, you must find a way."

Stoppani left the next day. On the way out, he held Maria for a long time and said, "I have every faith in you, my child." Acknowledging the difficulties that lay ahead, he conveyed his belief in her ability to overcome them.

Alessandro returned to his old self. Once again, he was head of his household, after sharing that role with another male, and a religious one at that, for an entire week.

It was the end of May and the end of Maria's last year in elementary school. She knew that most young women her age went on to convent schools to study music, poetry, and perhaps a language, and to prepare to become good wives, solid citizens, and mothers to a new generation of proud Italians. Some young women studied to become teachers. Maria had no interest in this. She was determined to go to engineering school, and there was no better time to tell her father.

Her mother had made zuppa di porcini, Alessandro's favorite, and they were finishing a pleasant meal. Maria announced, "Papà, I would like to enter the Regia Scuola Tecnica Michelangelo Buonarroti in the fall. My plan is to study engineering."

Alessandro wiped his mouth carefully and folded his napkin. He stared calmly at his wife and daughter. They shared the same luminous skin, the same determined chins, the same intense dark eyes. He glanced around the dining room and took in the calm, agreeable atmosphere. He thought with appreciation of the fact that his wife and daughter kept the house themselves, refusing help they could have easily afforded. There was a precision and equanimity to their lives that gave him, a military man, great comfort.

He cleared his throat and said, "During the Battle of the Volturno, the great Garibaldi, speaking to us, the troops that would have walked through fire for him, said that the greatest warriors choose their battles. This is a battle I am not going to fight. But I want you to know the greatest victory, for me as a father, will be to see you married with a home and many children, raising them to love God and the greatest country of all, Italy."

A darker tone came into his voice. "I know this idea comes from your Uncle Stoppani. I know that you have interpreted what the Pope said to mean that you can do whatever you like. I assure you, that is not what he meant."

Both Renilde and Maria remained quiet. Maria, too, knew how to pick her battles. Her father had given her permission to attend high school and continue her education. She understood this was against his wishes. She also felt that her mission in life, the one Pope Leo XIII had spoken of, would be much different than the one her father had suggested. But for the moment, she simply said, "Thank you, Papà."

On a sunny autumn day in October 1883, Maria Montessori began her education at the Regia Scuola Tecnica Michelangelo Buonarroti in Rome. Compared to her previous school, it was much larger, three four-story buildings flanking a courtyard with a fountain. It was also mostly male.

Her subjects of study for the next seven years would be Latin, Greek, mathematics, and science. This curriculum was set in stone and monitored by a centralized minister of education. The methodologies for imparting knowledge were all too familiar. Teachers lectured students, believing they were filling empty minds. Students memorized and repeated formulas and passages.

The school day went from eight o'clock in the morning until noon, and again from two o'clock until five. There was no physical activity whatsoever.

Maria managed to survive and thrive. She worked hard to excel at school. She used her free time to explore in depth the subjects she enjoyed. Before long, her parents allowed her to walk to and from school by herself.

The teeming city filled her senses. The area surrounding her school was being built up. Laborers from Southern Italy laid stone foundations and raised huge blocks to rooftops with pulleys. Beggars and their children, gaunt and thin, wandered the streets. Wealthy Roman women stepped from carriages as servants carried their belongings. Nothing escaped Maria's notice. Every detail was seared into her mind. She wondered why the world was so full of inequity.

On most days, when she returned home from school, her mother greeted her with a fresh semolina cake and a pot of tea. They discussed what Maria had studied during the day. Renilde teased out the most compelling aspects of a subject and often produced books from her own library that enhanced and deepened her daughter's interest. She asked Maria endless questions. They learned and laughed together.

Maria wanted to know more about the human body and how physical surroundings affect its growth. Renilde responded with encouragement. Alessandro grew accustomed to arriving home and seeing his wife and daughter huddled over anatomy charts spread across the table. Sometimes they became so absorbed that Renilde neglected to start dinner.

Maria did well in the first three years of technical school, earning 137 out of a possible 150 on the final exam, given in May 1886. She continued on to the Regio Istituto Tecnico Leonardo da Vinci, where she took Italian literature, history, geography, mathematics, and calligraphy.

Since girls were not allowed to mix with boys outside the classroom, Maria spent free periods alone in a separate room. She used this time to pursue her own interests. Increasingly, her focus turned to natural science and anatomy. By the time she graduated in May 1890, she had come to a firm decision. She would study medicine and become a doctor.

The fact that no woman in Italy had ever done such a thing did not deter her. Ever since she could remember, Maria had known she had a special mission. But it had never been clear to her until now. In her walks between school and home, she had observed tremendous need among the disenfranchised. She was consumed with questions about how society could help. She had an ability for math and science and empathy for the downtrodden. She wanted to make their lives better.

Maria was certain the only way to do this was to obtain a medical degree. She would have to inform her family, in particular her father, whose clear expectation was that she would become a wife and mother as soon as possible.

Final tests were over for all the students at the Regio Istituto Tecnico Leonardo da Vinci. It was early June 1890. The last evening rays of early summer sunshine spilled onto the dinner table of the Montessori family.

"I am proud of you, Maria," said Alessandro. "We should begin planning a graduation celebration."

"Papà, I am honored," Maria began. "I know that with graduation come thoughts of the future—"

Her father interrupted. "You will take the summer off. Take some time to see other young people your age. Even I believe that one can't work all the time, my dear." He grasped his daughter's hand and smiled at her across the table.

Renilde, who knew what was coming, crushed her linen napkin, kneading it in her lap. She and Maria had been practicing for weeks.

"Papà," Maria began slowly, "I have decided to continue with school. Medical school. I know I have a mission in life to help those who haven't had the advantages I have had. I've been blessed with a mind for science. I want to change the lives of the poor for the better. The way for me to do that is to become a doctor."

The convivial atmosphere turned cold. Alessandro Montessori stared at his daughter, then at his wife. His face bore a look of hurt and betrayal that quickly changed to anger. There was a short silence. They could hear the happy sounds of neighborhood children playing outside. A ball smacked against the pavement in a rhythmic pattern. Laughter and cheers floated through the open window.

"What does a nineteen-year-old know about a mission in life?" Alessandro exploded, purple with rage. "I will tell you your mission in life! It is to be a good wife and a good mother to your children. To raise them to be good Catholics, and to conduct themselves for the glory of Italy. To teach them, as I thought I taught you, respect for the wishes and wisdom of their elders."

His voice rose to a high pitch. "You have been spoiled and indulged by a mother who has failed to teach you proper respect!" Alessandro's open hand slapped the table. The china and silver jumped. "We are a military family. I am a civil servant. Do you know what this means? We are the example to others. What kind of example is this?"

The last sentence was spoken so loudly that the children outside the window were suddenly silent. The whole neighborhood had heard.

Renilde sat stone still. Her sweating palms had turned the napkin to a damp ball. Maria was now an adult, a graduate. Renilde knew that Maria would succeed with or without her father's approval. But it would not be easy. And once Maria left, Renilde would have to live with her husband. Renilde let her daughter speak for herself.

Maria remained calm, though shaken. "There is no one I respect more than you, Papà. And Mamma. I am who and what I am because of you. My strength comes from God. And from you. And I pray that it will see me through medical school."

They all sat in silence for a moment. Then Alessandro said bitterly, "I refuse to discuss this any further. I don't want to hear another word about it. You and your mother may do as you like. But don't ever speak to me about it again."

With that, Alessandro pushed back from the table. He gathered his coat and hat in the front hall and slammed out the door. His footsteps echoed on the stones below. The children resumed their game.

That night, Maria and her mother prayed for peace and understanding. The moon was full. Its light came through the lace curtains in Maria's bedroom. She sat upright in bed, listening for her father's return. Finally his steps came slowly into the apartment. It was very late. Alessandro knocked over the umbrella stand and swore loudly.

Maria heard the rustle of papers. Was he unrolling the anatomy chart? She climbed out of bed and tiptoed down the marble stairs. Alessandro was tracing the outlines of the chart with his finger and repeating the names of body parts to himself. In his way, he was trying to fathom the mind of a daughter he could no longer control.

Chapter Three

THE SOUL OF A DOCTOR

Guido Baccelli made his way quickly up the steps to the Santo Spirito complex. Situated between the Tiber and the Vatican, the ancient hospital was famous in all of Europe. It had humble beginnings in the eighth century as a resting place for pilgrims and later became an orphanage for abandoned children. As an institution, it was known as a place of protection and hope. Dr. Baccelli was always uplifted when he entered the complex and walked down the corridor past the magnificent library to his office.

Now sixty, Baccelli had the energy and focus of a man half his age. He was the minister of education for the newly reunified country. He had previously been the minister of agriculture, industry, and commerce. He was a pioneer in the use of the stethoscope. He had nearly single-handedly ended a malaria epidemic that had raged in Rome by draining the Campagna Romana and Pontine marshes and administering quinine to his patients.

He was a man of many interests, chief among them the University of Rome medical school and its students.

June was a busy month for the administrators. It was the time of year when prospective medical students applied for admittance. Baccelli interviewed each one. He had learned through the years to look over applications carefully. Grades and background were important. So, in his mind, was attitude.

An imposing, handsome man with an unruly shock of white hair, Baccelli always had a twinkle in his eye. He understood that the young men applying were often intelligent, youthful, and brash. Through the years, he had become skilled at identifying which ones had enough intelligence to succeed but not so much they would be intolerable to the faculty.

Baccelli settled in at his desk and looked over the list of that day's appointments. The first name on the list was Maria Montessori. Baccelli sniffed and assumed the second A was an O. "It must mean Mario," he thought. "There are no Marias in medical school. There are no women, period."

At nine o'clock precisely, there was a quick knock on Baccelli's mahogany door. He cleared his throat and commanded, "Come in, Mario."

He was shocked when a beautiful, raven-haired young woman entered. She was wearing a blue silk dress with an ivory fichu anchored by a cameo. She carried herself with confidence, moving into the center of the Turkish carpet that lay in front of his desk. She held a leather folder in one hand.

The morning light fell across her face. For a moment, Baccelli was speechless. Recovering, he asked, "Did you mean to volunteer at the hospital, Miss Montessori? That area is two corridors down. I know this is a confusing place."

"You are Dr. Guido Baccelli?" she said in a mellifluous voice.

She smiled broadly. Baccelli noticed her deep, dark eyes. He nodded.

"Then I am absolutely in the right place. I am here to interview for a place in the next class in the University of Rome Medical School. I want to become a doctor."

She stepped toward Baccelli, opened her folder, and gently placed it on his desk. "Here is my curriculum vitae."

Baccelli stared down at the folder. He used the moment to recover his wits. He thought he had seen it all during the years of his professional life. This was a new one.

The young woman seemed charming and intelligent. A quick glance at her CV revealed excellent grades, especially in math and science. There was nothing to do but humor her, at least for the moment.

They discussed some of Maria's former teachers that were known to Baccelli. He inquired about her father, whom Baccelli remembered from his time as minister of agriculture. Baccelli wondered briefly what this young woman's father, a civil servant and solid citizen, must think of his unorthodox daughter. He was silently grateful for his own two daughters. They were respectable Roman housewives with children of their own.

It was time to become serious. There were young men waiting to be interviewed. Baccelli sat up straight.

"Miss Montessori, you are a charming, intelligent young woman," he said. "But women are not doctors. We can't accept you in this or any class at the medical school at the University of Rome. Good day, and please give my regards to your parents." He stood up and bowed slightly.

Maria stood up as well. She stepped forward and retrieved the leather folder from Baccelli's desk. She tucked it under her left arm and leaned ever so slightly with her right on the edge of his desk. With great conviction, she said, "I shall become a Doctor of Medicine." She turned on her heel and walked quickly to the door, giving him a wide smile before closing it behind her.

Back home, Maria told her mother about her meeting with Baccelli. Neither woman was surprised. Renilde Montessori took out a sheet of paper. "We will make a list of every teacher you have ever had, everyone of importance or power who knows you or our family. We will write to them and request letters of recommendation, and we will deliver those letters to Guido Baccelli. You will be in the next class at medical school."

"Yes, I will," said Maria. "And I will write to the Pope."

They wrote until their hands cramped. The light of day faded and they barely noticed. The table filled with white envelopes. The sun had sunk behind the parasol pine trees outside their window when they heard Alessandro's heavy step. Laughing, they rushed to put away their work and prepare for dinner.

Renilde began heating a sausage stew and polenta. Maria gathered plates and silverware. They bumped into each other in their hurry and hugged for a long while. Renilde held her daughter and said, "You have a mission to fulfill. No one is going to stop you."

"Not with you at my side," Maria answered. Alessandro's key turned in the lock. He found them giggling like two schoolgirls with a secret.

Before long, letters of recommendation filled the mailbox. Renilde read with pride letters from former teachers, neighbors who were in the civil service, and clergy who had known Maria since she was a child. Only one teacher refused, citing that although he respected Maria, he couldn't support a woman becoming a doctor.

One day, a large ivory envelope arrived. It bore the seal of the Vatican. A note was attached to the outside. It clearly stated that the envelope was to be opened personally by Guido Baccelli. A meeting was arranged for the following day.

Baccelli was less friendly this time. He had already made his decision. He was annoyed at having to meet again. When Maria gave him the letter from the Vatican, his attitude changed from irritation to confusion. Maria watched while he broke the seal and read the letter. There was a long pause.

Finally Baccelli looked up. "Miss Montessori, I can't question the Pope. I am admitting you. I have no choice in the matter. But I will be watching you. You must prove, beyond the shadow of a doubt, that you have the strength to make life-and-death decisions about human beings. I will be honest. I don't think you have the strength or the stamina. I think you should be getting married and making a home."

Maria ignored the last part of his statement. "I will prove myself worthy of your trust," she said. "Today and always."

Baccelli had to smile at her earnest passion. For a moment, he was reminded of his own youthful idealism. "We shall see," he said.

On a gray autumn day in early November 1890, Maria began medical school at the University of Rome. Baccelli and the other administrators had insisted that her father escort her to class. They also ruled that Maria could not enter the classrooms or lecture halls until all the other students were seated. Since there was no precedent for a woman being in the class. Baccelli felt this might be the best way to proceed.

Alessandro Montessori reluctantly agreed to walk with his daughter to the university. He held her arm as they made their way down the sidewalk, wet with a recent rain. His lovely daughter gathered up the skirts of her dark blue silk dress to avoid the puddles as they crossed a street near the university. She held her head high. If she had any fear or trepidation, it didn't show on her face. Alessandro reflected that she had spent the entire summer reading thick anatomy and science tomes.

As they neared the entrance to the medical school, several young men lounged lazily against the door. They puffed on cigars. They crushed them out on the stone mane of one of the sculpted lions that flanked the entrance. They flipped the butts under trees that lined the sidewalk. They laughed uproariously at some joke as they jostled their way through the front entrance.

Alessandro kissed his daughter lightly, patted her shoulder, and wordlessly turned on his heel. Nothing could convince him this was a good idea. Yet he had to respect her determination. She would have to make her own way now. She was no longer a little girl. She was a young woman.

Maria stepped into a hallway. It was semi-dark. It seemed to go on forever. As her eyes adjusted to the dimness, she walked slowly toward the lecture hall at the end. Loud chattering came through the open doors.

Shelves lined the walls. She quickly realized they held jars of formaldehyde. Inside the jars, floating in a pinkish haze, were intestines and organs of all shapes and sizes. One long shelf held nothing but skulls. She thought, "All of these were once living, breathing humans with hopes, dreams, families, lives." As she advanced toward the lecture hall, she saw a human skeleton hanging from a wheeled rack near the arched entrance.

Totally unprepared for the sights and smells, Maria felt her stomach churn, just as she entered the massive lecture hall. There were ten rows of young men, with about twenty in each row. The chattering ceased immediately as Maria made her way into the hall. She had to walk in front of the entire assemblage and past every student.

All eyes were on her. The eyes weren't friendly. Maria thought she might be sick. It took every ounce of her will to keep going. The only empty seat was in the fifth row. She had to pass by ten young men to get to it. They refused to move or to make way as she squeezed past. She felt dizzy.

Maria gripped her stomach and sat down just as the professor, wearing a white lab coat, marched onto the raised platform at the front of the hall. He was pushing the skeleton before him. His hair was pomaded to a patent leather sheen. His eyes bored into the back of the room. He spoke in a stentorian voice.

"I am Professor Righetti! Welcome to anatomy, gentleman. And lady." Several heads turned toward her.

As the professor began to speak, Maria felt the attention gradually move toward him and away from her. She willed herself to take a deep breath. She pulled out a fresh notebook and forced herself to listen and take notes. As her fingers moved across the page, she felt her stomach muscles relax.

She completely understood everything Righetti was saying, and in many instances felt she could finish his sentences. She had already read and taken complete notes over the summer on the text to which he referred. She thought to herself, with great satisfaction, "I am here. I am at my first day of medical school. I am going to become a doctor."

Then she felt a kick at the back of her seat. Another. And another. She gave the perpetrator an angry look. He had blond hair that stuck straight up. He narrowed his eyes at her mockingly. Then she heard him hiss, "I must be immortal. Otherwise I would be dead from the look she gave me. Oh, was I kicking your chair? Please forgive me!"

Maria found the whole thing so ridiculous that she began to laugh. This was not what the young man expected. He grew very serious and said, "I am Luigi Pistone, and I don't think you should be here."

Without hesitation, Maria said, "I am Maria Montessori, and I saw you outside, smoking a cigar. My father would agree with you. He doesn't think I should be here either." She shrugged. "But here I am, and I'm going to stay, so you might as well get used to me."

Pistone puffed up his cheeks and made a loud blowing sound through fluttering lips. The air moved some of Maria's dark curls, which had come loose. "The more you blow, the higher I go," she said.

"Miss Montessori!" Righetti exclaimed from the front of the room. "Stand and tell us the Latin name for each of these, since you seem to be so full of energy and noise today."

With a pointer, Righetti began to slap various bones on the skeleton. "This is our good friend Dante. He has seen better days. But he is going to teach us a lot of things. Now, Miss Montessori. When I point, you tell us the name. Understand?"

As Righetti's stick bounced from bone to bone, Maria called out, "Cranium . . . sternum . . . manubrium . . ." She named every bone. It was an impressive display. If Righetti had meant to make an example of her, he had succeeded only in showcasing her intelligence and preparation.

He wasn't through, however.

"We have another talkative student right behind Miss Montessori. What is your name?"

"Luigi Pistone, sir."

"What are the chambers of the human heart, since you, too, seem so full of things to say?"

Pistone hesitated, dumbstruck. For some reason she would never understand, Maria took pity on him. She had the answers neatly written out from notes she and her mother had compiled. She slid the sheet of paper backward under her chair with the heel of her boot.

Pistone choked out the answer. "Uhhh . . . I have it in my notes, sir . . . Yes . . . Here. Upper left and right atria. Lower left and right ventricles."

At the end of the class, Pistone handed Maria's notes back. He had written a message at the top: "I was wrong about you. I owe you one." Pistone was a tiny man, about five feet tall. He was more casual about his education than some others. But he never forgot Maria's kindness. They remained friends all through medical school.

Maria's schedule that first day in November 1890 was typical of one she followed until she finished medical school. Her father escorted her to the university each morning. The course of study was strictly proscribed. It never varied.

Each summer, Maria and Renilde read through the texts for the next year. Maria made copious notes and was always among the most thoroughly prepared students. She took her education seriously. She already saw it as a stepping-stone toward making the world a better place for those who didn't have her advantages.

Some of her classmates were only going through medical school for the prestige it offered. A few didn't even plan to practice. The degree, for them and for their parents, was a status symbol.

During the school year, Renilde provided loving care for her daughter in the form of meals and constant encouragement. She went over the day's notes with Maria each evening and helped her prepare for examinations. After the first year, Maria's grades were so superior she received scholarships every year for the remainder of her time in medical school. In this way, she paid for her own education.

She had astonishing stamina and was able to attend medical school all day and study all evening. She was fascinated by the subject matter, even if it was presented in a rote manner.

Because of her gender, Maria was often isolated from her fellow students. For example, she was not allowed into the dissection room with her peers. Administrators couldn't abide the idea of a woman being present with a naked body, even a deceased one, among a group of men. She would have to do her dissection work at night, and alone. She was unprepared psychologically for the first dissection, which came during her third year.

Alessandro Montessori had instituted a strict rule, when his daughter began medical school, that they would not discuss her work or her studies. Nor could Maria and her mother discuss them in his presence. On the night of her first dissection, Maria asked her father to walk her to the laboratory. As was his custom, he didn't ask her about the purpose of her nocturnal visit. She didn't offer any information.

It was almost Christmas. Houses and businesses were decorated with festive lights and candles. Maria thought of her lonely task as her father walked beside her. Once she was safely inside the building, she waved to him through the window. He would return in three hours.

She had borrowed a cigar from her friend Luigi Pistone, thinking it might mask the smell of formaldehyde. She donned a lab coat and gloves and stepped inside the dissection room. There, on a table before her, was a deceased human being.

Maria lit the cigar and tried to take a puff, as she had seen Pistone and his friends do so often. The wind picked up outside. There was no sound in the lab except the scratch of a branch against the roof.

Maria slowly uncovered the body. It was a young woman with silky blond hair. Her face looked dewy and fresh. Maria had expected an old man. Not this. Not a young woman cut down in the bloom of youth.

The twin smells of formaldehyde and cigar smoke, combined with the sight of the body, were too much to bear. The loneliness and isolation of the past three years crashed in on her. Maria allowed herself to cry. Tears rolled down her cheeks, slowly at first and then in a torrent. Wracked by sobs, she ran out of the laboratory.

"I will never become a doctor. I can't do it!" she thought as she ran blindly down the street. Strings of Christmas lights blew in the wind. A poster of the Virgin Mary cradling baby Jesus was illuminated in a shop window.

Maria stopped when she saw a beggar woman sitting on the curb in front of the shop, now closed. She was wrapped in a thin, ragged blanket. A little girl sat next to her, holding a red strip of ribbon. Maria knew their plight far eclipsed her own.

Maria became fixated on the little girl, who sat on the curb in the squalid, dark street, playing contentedly with the ribbon. She folded it, unfolded it, and let it fly in the wind. She whirled it around her head. She laid it out, rolled it up, and watched it unfurl again. She smiled and laughed, unaware of her circumstances.

Maria thought, "If this child can find joy in a ribbon, then surely I, who have led a life full of privilege, can find joy and focus in my work." Her fear and sadness lifted. She returned to the laboratory and completed the dissection, more resolute than ever.

The holidays that year were especially happy ones for the Montessori family. Maria had a renewed sense of purpose that gave her great satisfaction.

In January, on the first school day after the holidays, a snowstorm struck. Most of Rome ground to a halt. The snow fell with such force that it seemed to sweep pedestrians from the street. Alessandro was stunned when he saw his daughter donning her heaviest coat and wrapping herself in layers of scarves.

"You are not going out in this. I forbid it!" he said.

"I have work due today, Papà, and a meeting scheduled about the assistantship at the pediatric hospital. Besides, I have to get used to it. Sick people don't follow a schedule or pay attention to the weather. When I am a doctor, I will have to go out in all kinds of weather and all kinds of conditions. I am practicing now."

Maria kissed her mother and closed the door to the apartment behind her. When she reached the street, she was nearly blinded by the snow. It hit her face like needles. Resting at intervals in shop doorways, Maria made her way slowly. A trip that normally took half an hour took twice that long.

She reached the medical school and walked down the hallway filled with jars, so familiar to her now. She greeted Dante the skeleton, which all the students did for good luck, and smiled as she thought back to her first time in the lecture hall.

The hall was almost completely empty. Not a single student was there. Professor Righetti sat writing at his desk on the platform at the front of the room. He looked at Maria as though he had seen a ghost.

"I live next door, so it was easy for me," Righetti said. "But you walked all the way? I can't believe it. You are the only student in the entire medical school who made it here today."

"We had an appointment. I came," said Maria, grinning. "Besides, as I told my parents, sick people don't have a day off."

"How true," said Righetti. "And how like you to think like that. Come to my office and let me make you some tea. You must be frozen stiff. And there is no need to discuss your assistantship at the pediatric hospital. The position is yours."

Maria marveled. Professor Righetti, the stern, pomaded examiner from her first day at medical school, had invited her to his office for tea.

His office was a mess, with books and papers piled everywhere, wilting plants, clothing draped over chairs, and dust balls in the corners.

"I apologize for the condition of my office," Righetti said. "My wife passed away recently, leaving me with four children to raise." He was suddenly much more human. Snow blew in through a window he had left slightly open. He rushed to close it. "I'll heat some water for tea. Please sit down, if you can clear a space."

Maria surveyed the chaos. "I understand your predicament,"

she said. "An ordered atmosphere is a helpful atmosphere. My father is a military man, and he taught me this. I'll help you make order here."

"I couldn't allow it," Righetti protested.

Indicating the storm outside, she said, "I won't be going anywhere soon. If we work together, we can create order here in no time. Besides, my sleeves are already rolled up."

They talked as they worked. Within an hour, they had created neat stacks from piles of books and papers. The floor had been mopped and the rug swept. The office had taken on an air of calm. And Maria had confessed to Righetti her growing interest in the field of psychiatry and pediatrics.

That spring, the medical students organized a festival of flowers at the Villa Borghese Gardens. Many of the city's wealthy families turned out to celebrate. Few failed to notice the lone woman among the men.

Maria Montessori stood out because of her gender. She was also exquisitely attractive and took great care with her appearance. That day, she wore a blue silk dress that matched the brilliance of the May sky. The white sash around her waist contrasted with her dark hair.

In 1894, Maria was chosen to present a bouquet of flowers and a banner to Queen Margherita, who was notoriously shy and didn't want to accept gifts from the students. Maria used her tact and powers of persuasion in a short speech. The gifts were graciously accepted. The students clapped and cheered. This was the first public speech given by Maria Montessori, then twenty-four years old.

Maria spent her final years in medical school studying, going to lectures, and working as an assistant at a pediatric hospital. She also assisted at a psychiatric hospital. In both positions, she gained clinical experience. Her peers had long since stopped teasing or challenging her. They had come to know her as an extremely dedicated, capable, serious person.

In 1896, Maria was at the top of her class. She had meticulously prepared for her profession. Only one hurdle remained before graduation. She had to defend her thesis, titled *A Clinical Contribution to the Study of Delusions of Persecution*, before a panel of ten administrators.

Maria Montessori passed her oral exam with a score of 105. Any score over 100 was considered extraordinary.

All medical students were required to make a speech on the subject of their thesis to the medical school. This would be Maria's first major presentation to a large crowd. She assumed her reception might be mixed and even expected some jeers. No woman had ever addressed this audience before. As she stood in the wings waiting to be announced, her heart was pounding.

Because of their agreement never to discuss medical school matters in his presence, Alessandro Montessori had no idea his daughter would be speaking before the entire medical school. On the morning of the speech, he happened to see a friend who asked him about it.

"What speech?" Alessandro asked. "I don't know about any speech."

"Good heavens, man! Your daughter is going to address the whole medical school. It's historic. Newspapers will be there. Photographers. This has never been done before. Don't you realize the significance?"

Alessandro decided not to go to work that day. Instead, he went to the University of Rome. When he arrived at the gates, he hesitated. He had walked to these gates every day for the past six years. But stubbornness and pride had prevented him from ever going inside with his daughter. He saw the jostling students and professors walking purposefully, clutching bags of books and papers. He had never entered the grounds.

He was compelled to do so now. He asked one of the students where the lecture hall for the medical school was located. He started down the long hallway, as his daughter had done six years before. To Alessandro, the lecture hall seemed huge.

There wasn't an empty seat anywhere. Alessandro had to stand at the back. The room was filled with a roar of chatter and expectation. Several photographers stood beside him, handling bulky cameras that clanked against the wall.

One man wore a fedora with a card saying "Press" tucked into the brim. He was tall and thin, and he spoke to a stocky red-faced colleague.

"Boss says some little woman is speaking here today. A woman doctor. Crazy! What will they think up next? A horse that talks? I hope this isn't a waste of my time."

"I don't think so," his friend replied. "This little gal is going to make history today. And I'm going to get the first scoop."

"I'll bet anything she's a homely horse-face," said the taller man. "Real women want to be at home and be wives and mothers."

Alessandro fought the urge to punch both of these men to defend Maria's honor. This was exactly what he had feared. A spectacle! But he had to admit he was fascinated by the magnitude of interest in his daughter.

Maria seemed to glide onstage as if she were floating on air. The crowd immediately hushed. She looked ethereal and breathtakingly beautiful. She wore a gray jacket and a large black hat that framed her face. She looked directly at the audience. She seemed to take in each and every person.

She graciously thanked the faculty and acknowledged her peers in the medical school, mentioning their high energy and sense of fun, which provoked appreciative laughter. She pointed out Dante the skeleton and asked for his blessing. She took command of the audience.

Her entire speech, on the subject of paranoia in mental illness, was fascinating and informative. No one moved or made a sound. The audience was rapt. The journalists standing near Alessandro took pages of notes.

Maria finished her speech with an impassioned plea for the humane treatment of people with mental illness. After a slight pause, the hall erupted in applause. The student body stood, clapping and stamping, until Maria came out for several more bows.

Alessandro saw a short young man with unruly blond hair bring his daughter a bouquet of flowers. He thought he saw him give her a box of cigars as well. He watched a crowd form around his daughter. The photographers pushed their way through. He saw his wife take his daughter's hand, standing by her side, as always.

Shame and regret welled up in him. He wanted to approach his daughter, but his feet were frozen to the ground.

At that moment, Maria looked up and saw her father for the first time. Ignoring everyone else, she walked toward him, arms outstretched. In a moment, they embraced. The tension and anger of the past years melted way. Dr. Montessori and her father were reunited.

～

Following Maria's graduation in July, the Montessori family held a reception at their apartment. Dr. Guido Baccelli attended, as did Professor Righetti and other faculty from the medical school. Military colleagues, family, and friends all gathered to honor Maria.

Her diploma was on display. The ornate document had to be altered to accommodate the female pronoun.

Maria navigated the evening with poise and grace, giving much credit to her parents. Baccelli stood up at one point and asked for the crowd's attention.

"I don't want to take too much time away from the person who should be the center of our attention tonight," Baccelli began. "I am grateful this extraordinary young woman has shown us all what women are capable of. She has proven me and many others wrong, and she has done so with hard work, dedication, and determination."

He paused, making sure everyone was listening.

"I would like to offer her a permanent job as assistant physician at San Giovanni Hospital," Baccelli continued. "Also, I would like to convey an offer for her to be Italy's delegate to the International Women's Conference in Berlin in the fall. I can think of no other woman in our country today who better represents the modern Italian woman."

There was a murmur of approval and excitement. Then Alessandro stepped forward. "My daughter has taught me that human potential is limitless, if one is willing to protect its growth," he said. "She has found her mission in life. This is only the beginning. Maria, I salute you."

Maria attended the International Women's Conference in Berlin in September 1896. In a speech that was widely reported, she urged everyone to support equal pay for women. She stressed the importance of assisting women with childcare needs. She challenged the notion of women as inferior beings and spoke of a bright and hopeful new century when more women would join the workforce and contribute to the betterment of society.

She championed independence for women. She stated that in her view of the future, women would have choices about marriage and childbearing. Their children would be taught to think for themselves, choosing peace over war.

It was a powerful, revolutionary speech that brought more than one thousand people to their feet. Journalists reported on the convention. Articles focused on Maria's speech and the positive reaction it provoked. Her photograph and accompanying articles appeared in international newspapers.

Maria returned to Italy as a young woman who was beginning to be known throughout Europe. Her progressive views on a woman's place in society and the welfare of children had been solidified by her trip to Berlin. She had a job, the beginning of a private practice, and a burgeoning international reputation.

But her challenges were not over. They were just beginning.

Chapter Four

THE SOUL OF A PATIENT

Early on a morning in October 1896, a loud knocking woke the Montessori family. Renilde reached the door first. She opened it to find a male laborer standing in the hallway. He was dressed in filthy overalls. Tears streamed down his face, and he huffed as though he had run a long distance. He removed a dusty cap and gripped it as he spoke.

"Please forgive me. But my wife, she has had twins. She is at home. Her bleeding won't stop."

Within minutes, Maria Montessori arrived at the door, fully dressed. She quickly put on a wool cape and picked up her doctor's bag, which sat ready next to the coatrack. She placed her hand on the man's shoulder and said, "Take me there. It will be all right."

The man was shaking. "No other doctors will come," he said. "All of my neighbors know about you. They told me to come here."

Renilde glanced at her daughter. All-hours interruptions

were becoming commonplace. Rather than exhausting Maria, they seemed to energize her.

Twenty minutes later, Maria and the new father, Rodolfo, had gone from the warmth and cleanliness of the Montessori apartment to a tiny basement dwelling in the slums of the San Lorenzo. The windows were shut tight. A film of grime blocked any light that tried to get in.

A thin, pale woman lay on a bed. She had no blanket. She was bleeding.

Maria looked quickly at the babies. Turning to the mother, she removed a stethoscope from her black leather bag. It was already scuffed from constant use. She listened to the mother's heart. It was beating wildly. Her blood pressure was low. Maria felt the young woman's stomach. It was spongy and had not yet retracted.

Rodolfo was keening in the corner. "What is your wife's name?" Maria asked.

"Her name is Carolina," he said between sobs.

Maria bent down toward the woman, whose eyelids were fluttering.

"Part of your placenta remains in your uterus, Carolina," Maria said. "It must be removed immediately. I am going to do that with my hand. It will be very painful, but only for a moment. I am going to give you my handkerchief. You can bite on it. Do you understand? I must cause you pain to help you. You have given birth to a healthy baby girl and a healthy baby boy. The one last part we can do together. Can we do it together?"

Carolina opened her eyes wide, locked them on Maria's, and gave an almost imperceptible nod. Maria took out a lace-trimmed handkerchief Renilde had given her. She wound it into a tight roll and placed it in Carolina's mouth.

She looked into her patient's eyes. There was only the here and now, and a connection between the two women that vanquished fear. Maria reached her hand into Carolina's uterus. Carolina arched in pain and fainted. Maria removed the rest of the placenta. The whole operation took less than twenty seconds.

Returning to the babies, Maria washed them in warm water. To check their responses, she rubbed them with a rough linen towel she carried in her doctor's bag. She swaddled both of them, setting them in the small fruit crates Rodolfo indicated were their cradles.

She removed the bloody sheet from the bed and washed it in a bucket of water she found near the small fireplace, hanging it on a nail to dry. Carolina stirred. Her quiet but steady breathing could be heard.

Rodolfo fell to his knees in gratitude. "It is a miracle!" he exclaimed. "You have brought my family back from the dead."

"I have done no such thing," Maria said, patting his shoulder. "Science and common sense have prevailed. Now, if I give you the money, will you go to the market for a chicken and some carrots? Carolina needs nourishment."

Within an hour, Maria had made soup in a dented tin pot. She fed Rodolfo. She swept the floor and washed the grime from the windows. Daylight flooded the small room. When Carolina woke, Maria fed her and helped the infants latch on to their mother's breasts.

"The girl will be called Maria, after you," Rodolfo promised.

Experiences like this one became common for Maria. She found the stamina to work at the San Giovanni Hospital during the day, caring for private patients, and minister to a growing number of nocturnal emergencies, almost always with patients who were destitute.

She developed a treatment method that took in the whole picture of the patient. She asked about the food they ate and the environment in which they lived. She often took it on upon herself to cook for her patients and clean their surroundings.

She gained a reputation among all her patients as an extraordinary physician who would go to any lengths for their care and well-being. Thank-you letters and gifts began to flood the Montessori apartment. Renilde kept all the letters in a wooden box in her bedroom.

Maria read everything she could find about medicine, mental illness, special education, and the new field of psychology. She was fascinated by the educational work and theories of two men, Jean Marc Gaspard Itard and Edouard Seguin. Both had worked with deaf and mentally challenged patients. In addition to her daily work with patients at the San Giovanni Hospital, she studied the work of these two French doctors. She sat at the dining table and translated their writings from the French.

Alessandro had to ask what was capturing her attention.

"Do you really want to know, Papà?"

"Of course I do."

"I'm reading the words of a Frenchman named Itard. He was a doctor and a teacher. But first, he was in the army."

"How did he get from the army to education?"

"Itard was a Provence-born banker who was forced to enter the army during the French Revolution. Though he had no training as such, he presented himself as a doctor and worked as an assistant physician at a military hospital."

"Those French will fall for anything. So he fooled his

superiors into thinking he knew something about medicine. What next?" Alessandro wanted to know.

"He eventually got a medical degree and was appointed to the National Institute for Deaf-Mutes in Paris. His specialty became otology. In 1789, he published an exhaustive work detailing the results of 170 cases. He developed a eustachian catheter and was one of the first doctors to diagnose Tourette syndrome. He was most lauded for his work with the deaf and the educational theories he developed from observation and experimentation with his patients."

Maria paused. Her father nodded. "Go on," he said.

"The most famous of Itard's patients was Victor of Aveyron. Victor was a feral child found in the forest near Saint-Sernin-sur-Rance. When he was discovered in 1800, his age was guessed to be twelve. He ran away from several villagers who tried to care for him.

"Victor had no language and behaved like an animal. He gave doctors an unexpected opportunity to study the relationship between man and nature, testing the French Enlightenment theory that every human being develops as a product of their nature and what surrounds them. They felt the Enlightenment notion of the 'gentle savage,' or the pure man existing ignorant of evil, could be proved by studying Victor. But Victor was uneducable, at least by the doctors who had first taken on his case.

"This is where Itard stepped in. He took Victor to his own home. He kept detailed reports on his progress. Itard believed that two things separate humans from animals: empathy and language. Victor made some progress, though not as much as Itard hoped. However, the methodologies and theories he developed, as well as Itard's analysis of Victor, opened the door to a new way of thinking about the education of deaf people."

Alessandro Montessori gazed at his daughter with admiration. "I am a military man and an administrator. A bureaucrat. Your facility for understanding and making sense of these ideas astounds me. Weren't you also learning about another fellow?"

Maria smiled. "Yes. His name was Edouard Seguin. Itard was influential in convincing others to go into the growing field of education for individuals with intellectual disabilities. Seguin was one of his followers. He studied and worked with Itard beginning in 1837.

"In 1840, Seguin started a private school in Paris for individuals with disabilities. He was passionate about developing systems for teaching them. He wrote extensively about this in a book called 'The Moral Treatment, Hygiene, and Education of Idiots and Other Backward Children.' It was the first textbook that detailed systems for working with such patients.

"Seguin emigrated to America in 1848 and started a number of schools there for the disabled. In 1866, he published a second book, 'Idiocy: And Its Treatment by the Physiological Method.' It focused on the importance of teaching self-reliance and independence to the disabled through a combination of physical and mental activities.

"Seguin was also influenced by the theories of economist-philosopher Henri de Saint-Simon, who believed that all of society should strive for the relief of the poorest and most vulnerable."

"So you are studying not only what these men discovered, but the systems they used in their work?" Alessandro asked. "This I can understand. Systems and observation. Gathering and using data!"

"Yes, Papà," Maria agreed. "That is it exactly. That is why I have been translating and studying their theories. I have had to translate over six hundred pages from the French. But I am so full of curiosity that each new discovery keeps me going."

"Well, it is now nearly one o'clock in the morning," said Alessandro, yawning. "Enough of these Frenchmen. I am begging you to go to bed, my child."

"I am no longer a child, Papà, but a twenty-eight-year-old woman with a responsibility to help others who aren't as fortunate as I am. Many of them don't have a loving mother and father, like I do."

"But you work constantly!" Alessandro protested.

"I don't see it as work, Papà," Maria said gently. "When you love what you do, it isn't work."

The next morning, Renilde found her daughter poring over her books. Maria had been up since dawn.

"What is this horrid drawing?" Renilde asked, leaning over Maria's shoulder to see what she was reading. "Is it a boy or an animal?"

"That is the question," Maria replied, "and you have asked it most succinctly. What separates us from the animals? That is the key to everything, and why I am so determined to understand. The drawing is of a boy found in the woods in France. Victor was a wild child with no language, and seemingly almost deaf. A French doctor named Itard worked with him exclusively for almost five years."

"Did Victor become civilized?" asked Renilde, intrigued.

"He made some progress. Itard's work, and Seguin's, is changing everything for me. It fits with all of my thoughts about how to reach my patients. It is inspiring me. And who knows? Perhaps the physical act of translation is helping me to retain this knowledge in my brain. So I'm not only learning, I'm experimenting on myself."

"What do you mean?" asked Renilde.

"I mean that by moving my hand across the page and writing the translated words, they are becoming a part of my thinking process. In any case, I feel this man Seguin was brilliant."

Maria Montessori made frequent visits to the mental hospitals in Rome. She found the conditions appalling. Patients of all ages and conditions, some mildly affected and others very severely affected, were crowded together in closed, airless rooms. They had nothing to do or see, no stimulation, and no physical activity.

One day while Maria was visiting a particularly depressing mental hospital, a female attendant pointed out, in a disgusted tone, that several of the patients were playing with crumbs they had picked up from the floor. A young girl of about ten was rolling crumbs of bread between her thumb and forefinger and placing them in a neat line on the stone floor.

Maria turned to the attendant and said, "They have nothing else to touch or interact with, no physical stimulation whatsoever. In desperation, they are using the only thing they can find in their environment. I consider that heroic. It is a creative act and shows she is capable of much more. Look around you. What would you do in this place?"

Maria thought back to what she was learning from Jean Marc Gaspard Itard and Edouard Seguin. She began to visit the hospital regularly. She chose ten children between ages five and ten. All had been assigned to the hospital because they were considered unreachable and couldn't function in a normal school. Maria examined them physically and took copious notes on their weight, height, age, and general health. A thorough record was begun for each child. It was updated daily so Maria could keep track of their progress.

She created a room within the hospital and brought in spools of colored fabric and stackable blocks in graduated sizes. She added fabrics of varying length and textures. The idea was to stimulate the children's interest through physical interactions with their world. Then Maria introduced the concepts of counting, using the same materials, and letter recognition, with letters cut from metal. In time, the students were tested. Their results were compared with those of ten children from a normal school. Many of Maria's students surpassed the so-called "normal" students.

Renilde was stunned by her daughter's success. "You have given these children and their families their lives back," she said.

"Mamma, you are kind. But I only set up an environment for them, and they did the rest. The potential was there. They just needed the right equipment and encouragement. They found the materials and interacted with them. And now there is something I wonder about."

"What is that?" asked Renilde.

"If this kind of stimulation and environment can work for a child with mental challenges, could it not work wonderfully well for normal children?"

"I can't imagine why not," said Renilde. "But that would take the work of a teacher, and you are a doctor, not a teacher."

"That is true," said Maria. As if to emphasize the point, someone knocked on their door. Alessandro went to answer it.

An anxious voice could be heard. Maria took one last bite of plaice, the oval-shaped fish her mother had made for dinner. She folded her napkin and hugged Renilde.

"Don't wait up for me," Maria said on her way out, holding her black doctor's bag. "I apologize that I can't help you clear the table." Renilde looked after her daughter with a mixture of pride and concern.

The end of the nineteenth century was a time of great interest in reform and progressive ideas in education and the treatment of women and children. Maria Montessori began to lecture on women's rights. She proved to be a popular speaker who approached her audience with a sense of humor and an uplifting message. She had a positive vision of the future, one where women who chose to work outside the home could do so, knowing their children would be nurtured by childcare systems while they earned a living.

A certain stratum of Roman society was ripe for Maria's message. These were women, mainly, who were wealthy. They empathized with the plight of the poor and felt it was their duty, as part of the privileged class, to support reform. They were progressives who saw poverty as an outgrowth of the lack of education. Some were Americans who had married into the Italian upper class. They got acquainted with Maria's work and ideas by reading newspaper articles, which appeared with increasing frequency, and by attending her lectures. Maria's message for the future of working women was always linked to the education of their children.

Before long, the general populace became familiar with Maria Montessori. Her fame, and the respect her patients had for her, caught the attention of the minister of education. He was seeking an administrator for a new school for mentally challenged children. He began to consider the notion that a woman could hold the position.

In early 1897, Maria was invited to apply for the position of director of the new Orthophrenic School in Rome. No woman in Italy had ever been put in charge of such an institution.

When she went for an interview with the minister of education, she found that his offices were near the entrance to the medical school at the University of Rome. She was early, so she walked past the stone lions into the building. She remembered with fondness her cigar-smoking peers. Eight years before, at this very same place, she had nearly thrown up. She recalled the determination it had taken to walk down the hallway.

The same jars sat on the shelves. They held the remnants of the physical human: the organs, fingers, and toes. Maria realized with a start that she would now be in charge of mental human capacity, the part that can't be put in a jar. The spirit. The soul. She would be in charge of trying to perceive and unlock the things that damage the human spirit and prevent it from achieving its potential.

She walked quickly down the hall. As usual, Dante the skeleton was hanging there. She shook his bony hand for good luck.

Chapter Five

THE SOUL OF A MOTHER

On a crisp spring day in May 1897, Maria Montessori made her way to the Orthophrenic School. It was attached to the University of Rome, a new facility housed in an ancient building. She wore a white linen dress with a lace collar her mother had made. She carried a large satchel with her favorite books on psychology and stacks of note cards that she planned to fill with daily data on each of her patients.

Her initial excitement about the position was tempered by the news that it would be a co-directorship. She would share the job with another physician.

His name was Giuseppe Montesano. She had met him briefly two years before, just after graduating from medical school. Maria remembered little about him except that he was male. She assumed the minister of education had not felt confident enough to give a woman total control. She thought of her father's saying, "Know when to pick your battles," and accepted the position without question. She did not feel that battling for sole directorship was worth it. She walked toward the entrance with cheerful confidence, eager to begin shaping a new mission for the school.

She arrived at her new office at eight o'clock in the morning, assuming she would be the first person there. She heard voices coming from an office down the hall. One was squawking loudly. She walked quietly toward the source of the noise and saw an open door. When she peered inside, she saw two people in profile. They were both seated on stools. The one on the right, dressed in a drab gray robe, was clearly a patient. The one on the left was a doctor. Maria recognized him as Giuseppe Montesano.

He was listening to his patient's chest with a stethoscope and speaking to him softly, trying to calm him. He took down notes on blue cards that looked exactly like the ones Maria used. The patient had Tourette's syndrome.

Montesano was so focused on his patient he didn't see Maria standing in the doorway. His jet-black hair was combed back from his wide forehead. He had a black beard and large, dark eyes. He made lengthy notes after each part of the examination, as Maria would have done. He treated the patient with the utmost care and respect.

After twenty minutes, he helped the patient stand, addressing him by his last name, and helping him to the door, just as a nurse came to take him back to his room. The doctor was startled to see a beautiful young woman dressed in white, watching him.

"Did you notice not only the repetitive nature of the sounds he made, but the way in which his symptoms subsided once he focused on breathing?" she asked.

"I did. Absolutely! And if you'll look at this . . ." He paused, sifting through his stack of note cards until he came to a specific one. He held it up for Maria to see.

"Yes!" she said excitedly. "That's precisely what I would have thought. What did you ascertain by the examination of the skull?"

"Ahhh . . . a most excellent question. Is there any specific reason you ask?"

"I noticed a difference, a slight tilt of the head to the left, which made me wonder about the vestibular senses."

"You must have read the newest article about vestibular sensory deprivation."

"I read it last year, when I was in Germany. I didn't know it had been translated. Once his breathing slowed as he focused on the stethoscope, once you allowed him to hold it and to participate in his own examination, he visibly relaxed."

"Exactly," Montesano agreed. "I noted that and thought perhaps introducing him to specific ways to focus might be of some help to him. By the way, I am happy to see you again. I have great respect for your work."

"Oh. Yes!" said Maria. "I guess we forgot about the pleasantries and got right down to work." Maria felt a deep sense of warmth. Her heart was pounding. Here was a colleague she could really speak to, one who seemed to understand what she was saying almost before she said it.

Their conversation about the patient continued for nearly an hour. They shared assessments and ideas about treatment options, detailing each possibility on the blue note cards. Finally, both had said what they wanted to say.

"Well," said Montesano with a smile, "that takes care of patient number one. There are only 299 left to go." He stood, bowed slightly, and continued, "Dr. Giuseppe Montesano, at your service."

Maria put out her hand, grinned, and replied, "Dr. Maria Montessori accepts. Let's call patient number two!"

They didn't need to engage in small talk. It was as if they had known each other for years.

A nurse brought in the second patient. She was a catatonic woman in her late teens. The two doctors gave her a thorough examination. They shared notation duties. Their stream of conversation focused entirely on the patient. They worked together like dancers who had been choreographed.

One patient followed another. Maria and Giuseppe worked without a break until the nurse pointed out that it was three o'clock in the afternoon. They had been working for nearly seven hours straight.

"It's what happens when you are doing something you love," said Maria. "But the work requires sustenance. I will see you at four o'clock." With that, she returned to her own office. She stared at her books and doctor's bag. They were sitting where she had left them early that morning. It seemed to her a whole new world had opened up since then. Outwardly, everything was the same. But her inner landscape was forever altered.

In Giuseppe Montesano, she had found someone who shared her mission, who seemed to understand and who could be a partner in changing the face of mental illness. But she felt more. Feelings she couldn't place as a scientist. As she ate the lunch Renilde had made for her, she stared out the window. She couldn't stop thinking about Giuseppe Montesano.

The two doctors worked tirelessly to examine and come to know each one of their patients, typically putting in twelve-hour days. Almost all of their conversation was about their patients. They rarely spoke of their personal lives. Driven by their shared mission, they worked to establish baseline examinations for all their patients. They made forays into the population to observe and take notes on their patients' daily interactions.

The constant, absorbing work was energizing for Maria. She arrived at home many days after seven o'clock in the evening, ate a meal prepared by her mother, then compiled reports about the patients she and Giuseppe had seen during the day.

It quickly became Maria's habit to stop at Giuseppe's office each morning when she arrived at the Orthophrenic School, to report on her previous evening's research.

"I am in awe of the way in which you work all day here and then go home and put in four more hours, translating and studying," Giuseppe once said.

"God gives me strength for the mission," Maria replied, smiling. "That, and my mother's cooking." Then she launched into her report. Giuseppe was all ears.

One morning in June, Maria knocked on Giuseppe's door, opened it, and saw an older woman seated in a chair next to Giuseppe.

She was definitely not a patient. She was dressed in an elegant black silk skirt and blouse. She wore an ermine cape, despite the heat, and a large black hat with white feathers that framed her face. Turning toward Maria, she held her chin high and stared at her wordlessly through pince-nez, which gripped the sides of her thin, patrician nose. Her long, bony fingers wrapped around the marble top of a cane.

"Dr. Montessori," said Giuseppe, speaking formally, "this is my mother, Margarita Montesano."

Giuseppe's mother sat stiffly, regarding Maria, and finally said "Good morning," as one might to a servant. Then she turned her attention back to her son, who looked awkwardly from his mother to Maria.

"I won't disturb you," said Maria graciously. She was about to leave when Giuseppe's mother said, "My son has a delicate constitution. He works too hard. I don't understand why he wants to work in this filthy city with a population of idiots. He is descended from the House of Aragon. He could be living with us on our estate in the country and treating normal patients." Her tone implied that Maria was somehow responsible for Giuseppe's decisions.

Maria said calmly, "Our work inspires us. And perhaps your son is finding strength in the progress and healing of some of our patients."

Margarita stared at Maria through narrowed, beady eyes. Maria thought of the crows that liked to perch on her mother's clothesline. Margarita gripped and re-gripped her cane. She said nothing. The room filled with a cold silence.

"Good day," said Maria, nodding politely. Once in her office, she tried to understand what had just happened. It was shocking to see her colleague reduced to a mute state by his mother. Since they rarely discussed their personal lives, Maria had no idea about his aristocratic background. And no more time to consider it. The nurse was already at her door with the first patient of the day, a Mr. Luciano, who presented with nervous tics.

Maria worked the entire day, seeing patients as usual. She avoided passing Giuseppe's door. Early in the evening, a light rain began to fall. Wind whistled down the hallway. For once, Maria felt exhaustion deep in her bones.

The storm grew in intensity. It was almost seven o'clock. She had been at work since eight in the morning. The hospital was quiet. All the other employees had gone home. Without interacting with Giuseppe, the day had seemed long.

Maria began to pack her satchel with books and papers for her evening study session. She looked for her umbrella, anticipating walking home in the storm. She heard a knock at the door. It was Giuseppe.

"I wanted to give you notes on your first patient, Mr. Luciano," he said. "I apologize that you didn't have them this morning, as they were in my office."

His apology seemed to be about other things, but Maria accepted it with a nod. It was such a relief to see him. Her heart was pounding crazily.

"Let me find my notes so we can put them together," she said. Hurrying to her desk, she tripped over a rug, hit her head on the side of her desk, and sprawled on the floor.

Giuseppe raced to kneel by her side. He gently lifted her head and said, "You've cut yourself. A small cut. But it is bleeding. Don't move. It is right on your jawline."

He reached for Maria's medical bag. "It is all right if I use it? It is much neater than mine!" he joked, rummaging inside with one hand. He held her head with the other. He leaned over her and put her head in his lap. He touched her cheek and jaw and began to dab at her cut.

She looked up at his brown eyes, full of concern. His hands were warm and his touch made her heart beat so loudly she thought it would burst from her chest. She could smell the wool of his coat and the lavender in the starch of his shirt. The physical act of being cared for in such a quiet, kind way was transporting.

Their eyes met, and Maria felt the softness of his lips on

hers. Giuseppe kissed her cheeks, her forehead, the cut on her jaw. He slowly undressed Maria. Part of her felt the warm hands, the soft touch, the embrace. Part of her floated above and saw herself as a child, releasing the butterfly from the dome. The beauty, the pleasure, the freedom of the moment settled into her soul. They created a oneness where there had been two.

And then the moment was over. Giuseppe dressed quickly. He wrapped Maria in a shawl that hung on her coatrack. He knelt down and said, "Are you all right?" His tone seemed slightly removed.

"Yes," she said. "I am all right."

"I must go to meet my mother," he said, looking at his pocket watch. He turned her head once more to look at her cut. His hands were no longer warm.

"I am predicting it will heal nicely, with no scar. I will see you in the morning, Dr. Montessori."

The storm had ended. The last rays of evening light were setting behind the edifice of the medical school. Maria walked home slowly, as if in a trance. The whole world had changed. And yet people still rushed about as if everything were normal. There was an orange and pink glow in the sky. The streets glistened, swept clean by the wind and rain. Some leaves had already begun to fall from the trees, signaling the coming autumn.

"You look so tired," Renilde said as Maria entered the apartment. "Are you all right?" It was the second time in an hour that someone had asked her this question.

"Yes. I am all right. I will be all right. Everything will be all right," Maria said.

Six weeks later, Maria knew she was pregnant. She and Giuseppe had never referred to what happened between them on that rainy day. Instead, their work took on a feverish pace. They typically worked fourteen-hour days.

Maria was using ideas she had gleaned from Itard and Seguin. She introduced letter cutouts for patients to trace, colored beads for them to string, lacing boards and other materials for them to manipulate. The success of her work drew the attention of other professionals. She began to lecture frequently about her philosophy of education for her patients. She also taught the first classes for teachers and other colleagues who wished to emulate her success.

Respected as a doctor, an administrator, and a lecturer, Maria Montessori, age twenty-seven, was at a high point of her career. She had earned the respect of her peers and was beginning to have an international reputation as a crusader for the rights of women and children. She was also unmarried and pregnant. She would be a pariah, shunned and scorned, if Roman society learned her secret.

In late October 1897, the leaves on the plane trees outside Maria's office were beginning to turn. Giuseppe and Maria had just finished writing a report about the successful treatment of a formerly mute eleven-year-old girl who was now able to attend a regular school.

"Before we stop today I must tell you something," Maria said. "Straightforwardly, as there is no other way. I am going to have our child in March. And yes, I am all right."

Giuseppe's look of love and concern touched her to the core.

"I have never known anyone like you," he said. Words spilled out as if he had been keeping them bottled up. "Your intelligence, your inspiration, the wealth of your knowledge. I will write to my mother immediately. I will try to make her accept you. We can raise our child on my family estate, surrounded by grandparents, aunts, and uncles. You will make a glorious mother. Everything will be taken care of for you. You won't have to do anything at all, ever again, but be with our child." His eyes were shining.

Maria was stunned. She understood that Giuseppe was only doing what generations of males before him had done. She couldn't blame him. He was trying to do what he thought was right. But underneath was the assumption that she would abandon her life's work, her mission, her God-given capabilities, her hard-fought independence. She prayed that she would find the right words. She knew, without equivocation, that she was going to continue her work. Nothing was going to stop her.

"You are a good man," she began, speaking slowly and deliberately. "You are a kind man. And we are creating, in this hospital, methodologies I believe will help future generations of patients to lead better lives.

"I know you are offering what is honorable. But I cannot and will not abandon my mission in life. I believe I am not normal, and I give God credit for my abilities. I am an abnormal woman teaching abnormal children. It is meant to be. It is, for me, the natural order of things."

There was a long silence. Through the open window, they could hear the autumn leaves scuttling along the sidewalk.

Finally Giuseppe said, "I respect you, Maria. I will always love you. I do love you. But I can't break my mother's heart. I can't stain the honor of my family by marrying someone of whom they cannot approve. My mother would never accept a daughter-in-law who, as she puts it, works with imbeciles. You would have to abandon your life here and live with my family.

"If you won't do that, I am afraid there is no alternative. I will never marry another. The child can take my name. We can continue our work here. You understand, don't you? I couldn't do this to my mother, to my family."

"I understand all too well," Maria said calmly. "If our marriage means that I have to give up everything I have worked for, we will not marry. I will have our child away from here. I will find a family who can raise our child. There is no other way. Our souls and our intellects are already one. Now we will have a child who represents that wholeness. We will have to be satisfied with that."

"You are certain of this?" asked Giuseppe. He was ashenfaced.

"I am certain. It is the only way."

Giuseppe stood and walked to the door. He turned and said, "I will never love another woman as I love you." He left, closing the door behind him.

Maria was scheduled to travel to London to address a women's congress, as she had done after her graduation from medical school. She had become the preeminent Italian spokesperson for the rights of women and children. In London, she spoke eloquently on these themes. She focused specifically on egregious child labor practices, particularly in the mining industry. Eliminating child labor in the mines and strengthening laws relating to this practice was a cause of Queen Victoria. Knowing that she would soon have her own child, Maria spoke with renewed passion. She had an audience with the queen that was widely reported and photographed.

Maria was at the height of her powers in many ways. She was also experiencing daily nausea and the burden of carrying the secret of her pregnancy alone. When she returned to Rome, Alessandro and Renilde prepared a special welcome home dinner. Renilde made her favorite foods, but Maria barely touched them. Renilde noticed but said nothing.

At the end of the meal, Alessandro brought out a large square object wrapped in tissue paper. "A gift from me to you," he said, "although your mother wrapped it. I am no good at such things."

It was a hand-tooled leather scrapbook. Inside was every article, every photograph, every accolade Maria had received, beginning with her graduation from medical school. Her father had saved it all.

Maria was deeply touched. The secret she was carrying and the love expressed by the gift overwhelmed her. She broke into tears and couldn't stop. Her shoulders heaved. Both of her parents took turns comforting her: a mother who understood intrinsically that there was something behind the tears, and a father who patted her shoulder in bewilderment, saying, "There, there, now!"

Later that night, after her father had gone to bed, Maria came into the living room. Her mother was knitting, as she often did in the evening. Maria recalled happy times sharing this activity with her mother. The tears earlier had acted as a sort of expiation, but she knew it was time to turn to the person in her life who understood her the most. She knelt down beside her mother.

"What is troubling you, my dear one?" Renilde asked, laying her knitting aside.

"I am going to have a child," Maria said simply. "The father is Giuseppe Montesano."

Renilde showed no surprise. "Do you love him?" she asked.

"Yes. And I always will. He is the father of my child. But I can't be his wife."

Renilde took her daughter's hand. They talked for hours, until dawn's first light made the lace curtains glow.

Later that day, Renilde contacted a convent she knew just outside Rome. It was where she had gone to school, and she knew it well. Maria went into seclusion there in her seventh month of pregnancy. It was the first time in nearly six years that she had stopped working with patients daily. She continued studying the work of Itard, Seguin, and other educators.

Maria and Renilde kept the pregnancy secret from Alessandro. Renilde explained Maria's time at the convent by saying that Maria needed a rest. Alessandro heartily agreed; he had been encouraging his daughter to rest for some time.

On March 31, 1898, Maria began to feel contractions. She timed them with her own watch. Her labor didn't last long. Just before midnight, Maria Montessori gave birth to a healthy baby boy with a shock of dark hair.

Adrenalin pulsed through her veins and muscles and gave her involuntary shivers. Maria saw the crisp white sheets, the warm wool blanket that wrapped her son, and the two nurses who stood watch. She thought of the thousands of women who gave birth in filthy circumstances with no support or sustenance. She knew this child would always be loved and cared for. She wanted this for all mothers, for all children. She knew that God had given her this mission in life.

She gazed at her son and remembered what Dr. Baccelli had called her, the masculine name he had mistaken for hers. "I will name you Mario," she said. "Of your mother, and yet your own person. The masculine form of Maria." She gently kissed his forehead and whispered, "You will be protected until you are ready to fly, my little Mario."

Maria spent another four weeks with her infant son. Then the day came to leave him with the young farm couple who would care for him. He would be an hour outside Rome in a small village, a short train ride away.

Unable to sleep the night before, Maria walked outside. It was an early spring night. The full moon shone on the almond trees in the garden, just beginning to show their buds. She looked up at the sky and saw Ursa Major, the bear. The firmament was alive with stars. She knew that God had given her the gifts she possessed, and she had faith that God would continue to bless her. She prayed for the safety and comfort of her infant son, and of all children and their mothers.

Maria visited her son as often as she could, given her heavy schedule of lecturing, teaching, and seeing patients. Giuseppe was overjoyed that Maria had given birth to a healthy son. He didn't ask much about Mario, and this hurt Maria deeply. She hid her feelings so she could go on working with their patients.

It broke her heart every time she had to say good-bye to Mario after a Sunday visit. But she was strengthened by the response to her speeches. She traveled throughout Europe, championing the rights and freedoms of women. She rejected the notion that women were inferior. She offered increasingly pragmatic and specific solutions to the problems of child labor and poverty. More and more, these solutions centered on education. She rarely used notes when she spoke.

Audiences who came expecting a dry, pedantic speaker were

pleasantly surprised to see a young woman who was fashionably dressed and who framed her opinions in a way that was digestible and relatable.

Mario was never far from her mind. She was constantly aware that she was giving up raising her own son so she could help other mothers and children. The combination of the spiritual and the scientific in Maria's speeches turned many who came to listen into fervent followers. They were attracted not only to the substance of her message, but to the person delivering it. Maria wasn't just informing them about her work and opinions. She was inspiring her listeners to do their own work and have their own opinions.

The Orthophrenic School was a teaching institution, and in her role there, Maria influenced not only patients but also future doctors.

Maria took strength from knowing that Mario was being well cared for. Her visits to him in the following year confirmed this. She continued to confer daily with Giuseppe about patients. But something was broken between them. Although they maintained a professional relationship, they rarely spoke of personal matters. Giuseppe praised Maria's insights about patients and continued to marvel at her stamina. But he seldom asked about Mario and did not seek to visit him.

Giuseppe always spent the Christmas holidays at his family home. Just before leaving, he said to Maria, "I want you always to remember, no matter what happens, that our souls are one. Sometimes we have to fulfill our responsibilities to our elders. Sometimes our lives cannot be our own."

Maria answered swiftly, "You are wrong about that. As long

as I am alive and breathing, my life is my own. I want to help my patients and students believe this about their lives. But how can I do that if I don't set an example? Their lives are their own. Yours is. Mine is."

Maria and her parents celebrated the turn of the new century together, traveling to the hills above Rome to watch fireworks. Arm in arm, they walked home.

Alessandro Montessori turned to his daughter and said, "There are many times we have clashed. And many times I haven't understood your stubbornness and saw it as willfulness. I now know I was wrong. You are a person for the new century. I will never question you again."

Maria was full of love for her father. She wanted to tell him about Mario, to unburden herself and let her father know that he had a beautiful grandson. She saw that Renilde understood her longing. Renilde shook her head softly. The moment passed.

Maria returned to work at the Orthophrenic School in early January. On her first morning back, she began going over the list of the day's patients. There was a knock at the door. Expecting Giuseppe, Maria stood up to answer it.

She opened the door to find Giuseppe with his mother and a petite blond woman. The women wore fur coats with matching fur caps.

"The Montesano family wishes the Montessori family a happy New Year," said Margarita Montesano. Her eyes glittered beneath her hat. "May I also present my new daughter-in-law, from a family that our family has known for years. She and Giuseppe were married a week ago."

Maria was so shocked she thought she had heard wrong. She looked at Giuseppe. He stood stiffly in the doorway and said nothing. His arm was under the elbow of his new wife. The blood in Maria's ears made a rushing sound, like an ocean wave. For a moment, Maria felt as though she might faint.

"My husband has great respect for you and I am honored to meet you," Giuseppe's new wife was saying through the roar in Maria's ears. "We have brought you a bottle of wine, made in our region, as a gift." She held out a small damask bag tied with a ribbon. Maria took it and managed to murmur "Thank you."

"We know you have patients to see, and we will leave you in peace," said Margarita. "Happy New Year, Maria Montessori." With that, she turned and led the entourage down the hall to her son's office.

Maria closed the door and leaned against it for support. A patient was due to arrive at any moment. How could she possibly face a patient? How could she go on breathing, moving, living? How could a man who was so kind, so understanding, so empathetic with patients do something like this?

She began to walk to her desk. The damask bag slipped from her grasp and fell to the floor. The bottle inside shattered, and wine soaked through the bag onto the rug. Maria stared. Then practicality took over. She found a rag, sopped up the liquid, and rinsed out the rag, over and over. She scrubbed the blood-red mark until all traces disappeared. She picked up the bag with the glass inside and threw it in the trash. She opened her window and let the January air fill the room. By the time her first patient arrived, the wine smell was gone. Dr. Montessori was at her desk, shaky but resolute.

Her first patient was a young woman of thirty. The same age as Maria.

"I have suffered a recent trauma," she said.

"I understand," said Maria. "Tell me more."

And so the day began.

~

Her walk home in the January twilight took her by the University of Rome. She stopped and stared at the stone entrance gates. The knowledge she had gained there about anatomy and the physical aspect of medicine had allowed her to begin her practice. In the years since, she had lectured in cities all over Europe about equality for women and the importance of education for the masses. She found herself, on this day, at a crossroads in her life.

She put Giuseppe's marriage into the context of society at that time. She knew that for women, there were few choices. His mother was only doing what society dictated aristocratic mothers should do. And the young wife, who Maria ruefully realized had not even been introduced by name, was only doing what most aristocratic young women did.

Maria understood that it was her duty, her mission, to show the world a different picture of what a woman could do. She could no longer work and teach at the Orthophrenic School. It would be intolerable to work with Giuseppe now. And she had a strong desire to understand more about human behavior. She wanted to study anthropology, philosophy and the new field of psychology. Maria went into seclusion at the convent where she had given birth to Mario. When she returned, she tendered her resignation at the Orthophrenic School. She had decided to go back to school.

It was the dawn of a new century. If circumstances dictated that she could not raise her own child, she would spend the rest of her life helping other women and children become free from the constraints she faced. She was sure of her mission, but not of the specific path it would take.

Chapter Six

THE SOUL OF A STUDENT

Maria Montessori returned to the University of Rome in the fall of 1901. In contrast to her first experience there, the anthropology and philosophy departments, in addition to the new experimental psychology department, were welcoming and had both male and female students.

The experimental psychology department was run by Giuseppe Sergi. He based many of his theories on scrupulous measurement and observation, a habit he had learned from his teacher, Cesare Lombroso.

Maria was trained by her professors to rely on observation and thorough analysis of the data gathered from that observation. Because of her training in scientific methods, she differed from most other theoreticians, especially those in the realm of education. She remained, for many years, one of the only female educational theoreticians who came from a medical background. Maria's studies in the departments of anthropology and psychology underscored for her the importance of observation and analysis.

As part of her education, Maria observed elementary classrooms in Rome. They were as restrictive as Maria remembered from her own childhood. Children sat on hard chairs or benches, listening to teachers who stood stiffly at the front of the classroom giving rote lectures. The style of educating children had not changed. Maria was appalled by what she saw as another generation of students being inculcated into an educational system that diminished, rather than encouraged, independent thinking and self-motivated learning.

Because she came from a medical background, and because she already had a high public profile, Maria was bound to stand out in the department. She was the only student with a medical degree and her own medical practice. Soon she was asked to begin lecturing. Students used to single-focus lectures given by the same professors year after year flocked to her lectures.

Maria used a multidisciplinary approach, drawing from her background as a scientist and doctor, her pedagogy with patients, her years of experience observing hundreds of patients, and the many lectures she had given. Her practical experience and her viewpoint as a woman captivated students at the University of Rome. Their reaction was similar to that of audiences who heard her speak in cities across Europe. They were inspired as well as educated.

In 1906, a young woman named Anna Maccheroni attended one of Maria's public lectures. She was not a student at the University of Rome. She was a sensitive person who had begun to formulate her own visions of how the educational system could be changed.

Anna Maccheroni was from an educator's family. Her father was a teacher who followed the theories of Froebel, a renowned German educational theorist who invented kindergarten. Anna had grown increasingly critical of the Italian education system and had stopped teaching in protest. She could no longer support a system she felt failed students so thoroughly. She was discouraged and disheartened with her chosen profession when she read that Maria Montessori would be giving a lecture. She decided to attend out of curiosity.

Anna was in her early twenties and had just begun to recover from a bout of depression that left her unable to work. Her parents had recently divorced, a scandal in society at that time, and she felt shunned and isolated. She considered moving to America to start over, but her shyness made this a daunting notion.

This was Anna Maccheroni's frame of mind when she entered the lecture hall. She had little idea of what to expect, other than knowing the speaker was a woman and a medical doctor with new ideas about education. She sat in the audience of students and professors, feeling ill at ease and out of her element.

Maria Montessori was introduced by Professor Sergi, the head of the school of anthropology. She came slowly onstage, commanding the attention of the entire audience. A hush fell over the crowd. She wore navy blue silk and a striped blouse accented by a crisp white collar and cuffs. Her wavy dark hair was coiled into an elegant chignon. She looked at her audience with expressive eyes, taking them all in, as if to say, "I know you are all here and you are all important." After acknowledging

Professor Sergi and the departments of anthropology and experimental psychology, she began to speak.

The soothing quality of her voice caught Anna by surprise. There was not a trace of stridency. The warmth and passion of her cadences were captivating.

Maria began by addressing what she believed should be the hopes and dreams of all educators: to create a peaceful world with the opportunity for every person to reach his or her highest potential. She spoke of the vast possibility of each human being to affect others. She spoke at length of the specifics of her work with the mentally challenged, and the importance of activity, physical connection, and spiritual connection to their teachers and the natural world.

Maria encouraged the women in the audience to see themselves as leaders and as people who could join the workforce and still have children. She spoke as a proud Italian, but also as a citizen of the world who viewed education as something for all, with self-motivation and independence as the ultimate goals.

In conclusion, Maria asked each person in the audience to think of corals. Tiny as they are, they form new islands and continents. Perhaps in a nod to her own circumstances, she acknowledged that not everyone can know at all times exactly where life will lead. She explained that the pursuit of a mission begins with knowing that our actions have great effect. She was fervent in the belief that the purpose of life was not simply to enjoy oneself, but to make the world a better place.

The entire audience rose to their feet in an ovation at the end. Maria bowed her head and brought out Sergi, insisting that he also take credit. The audience, mesmerized and inspired, wanted more. A huge crowd formed around Maria.

Anna Maccheroni sat perfectly still in her chair, amazed

by what she had heard. Here, at last, was a voice and a leader with a message Anna understood and could relate to. It was as if she had been waiting her entire life to have these thoughts articulated. She had begun to give up hope that her ideas about education had any validity. Now she knew better.

She sat for a long time, gazing at the swirl of people around Maria Montessori. Then she gathered her coat and hat and began to walk home. A light rain was falling, but Anna barely noticed it.

When she reached home, her father immediately saw the change in her demeanor. For months, she had been depressed and listless. Now she seemed full of energy and hope. He was impressed as she told him about Maria's speech. Many of its concepts were compatible with his own, especially regarding early childhood education.

"You must try to meet with her and tell her about your admiration and your ideas," her father said.

"I could never do that!" Anna protested. "She is a busy person, an important person. Besides, why would she ever want to meet with me?"

"Even visionaries need assistants," he said. "They can't do it all alone. And you have visions and ideas of your own that I think she would welcome."

"What would I say?" Anna wondered. "The thought of it terrifies me!"

"That is exactly why you must do it," her father urged. "You must take the chance, my dear one. It is not for yourself. Think of the children whose lives you want to change."

Anna wrote to Maria, asking for a meeting. Several weeks later, a response came on thick cream-colored paper. Maria had invited Anna to her home. The note was written in neat blue

THE SOUL OF A CHILD

script and signed by Maria herself. Anna clasped it to her breast with excitement. She knew it was childish, but she slept with it under her pillow.

The appointed time was a bright spring evening in May. On the way, Anna Maccheroni had second thoughts. What would she say to this powerful, intelligent woman? Why had she dared to ask for her time? She feared she would be unable to speak a word.

Renilde Montessori answered her knock, introduced herself as Maria's mother, and led her upstairs to the second-floor apartment. Anna was amazed that there appeared to be no servants. Renilde brought her a cup of tea, seating her in a chair in the hallway. She apologized that Maria was running late. She was finishing a meeting and would be with Anna momentarily.

A large mirror hung on the wall opposite the chair where Anna sat. She gazed at her reflection. Her face was incredibly thin and her hat was askew. She thought she resembled a bedraggled sparrow. What could she possibly say to this elegant woman? Why had she come? She began to consider running away. Anna was shaking so much her teacup rattled in the saucer.

Suddenly a door in the hallway opened and an officious-looking man stalked out. He was tall and thin and seemed to be in a hurry. He did not acknowledge Anna. She could hear the door to the street slam below.

Maria's head appeared from the doorway. "Edoardo Talamo is always in a hurry," she said, laughing. "And so dramatic! Yes, he is the head of the Roman Association for Good Building, and yes, I know he is busy. But he seems bent on letting everyone else know how important he is ... Forgive me! Here I am, prattling on, and you must be Anna. It is so kind of you to come. Your letter touched me. I am Maria Montessori. Please come in and let me know how I can help you."

Maria's warm greeting and sense of fun dispelled Anna's fears. She felt as though she were meeting an old friend.

The two women sat together on a small velveteen sofa.

"What brings you here, my dear?" Maria asked. "You wrote that you are a teacher and have studied Froebel. I have, too, and I would love to hear what you found useful. Tell me what I can do for you."

"I am not exactly sure, Dr. Montessori," Anna replied. "I am at a crossroads."

"There is nothing wrong with not knowing the next turn in the road. And you may call me Maria. I appreciate your candor, and I will be candid with you. I, too, am embarked on something, and I am not certain of the outcome. But I feel I am on the right path. I went back to academia to study anthropology, philosophy, and experimental psychology. I have complete faith that it is all part of a greater purpose. God has given me these gifts, and it is my job to use them for the betterment of others, especially those who haven't had my advantages."

"What are those advantages?" Anna asked.

"First and foremost, loving parents, and especially a mother who has believed in me. She believes that I, as a woman, can accomplish anything. Her strength and support have meant the world to me."

At this, Anna's eyes filled with tears. She began to weep, at first quietly, and then with heaving sobs. Maria gave Anna her handkerchief and sat patting her back.

When Anna was able to speak, she said, "I didn't come from a family like yours. My parents argued and fought constantly.

My father wanted to put his educational ideas into practice by starting his own school. My mother didn't want him to. That was the source of most of their battles. They got a divorce, which is so unusual, and now many of the neighbors won't speak to my father and me. I feel like a pariah. My mother moved away because I agreed with my father. I wanted to take his ideas and make something of them. Now my father is a broken man. I love teaching, but I can't teach in this system because I feel it is morally wrong. I have been broken down, weakened, and that is why I stopped teaching . . . why I have been . . ."

Anna looked into Maria's eyes. They were full of kindness. She had no fear of continuing. "I had become depressed. So depressed I couldn't think, couldn't move, or find any joy. I felt I might never be able to contribute to the world. Until I heard you speak. Then I felt renewed. Understood. As though there was someone in the world who shared my hopes and dreams, who could put words and actions to them."

A tiny smile appeared. "Do you think I am crazy? I have never spoken this long to anyone in my life."

"You are not crazy," Maria said. "You have encountered sadness, challenges, and difficulties. Although I have a loving family, I, too, have encountered heartbreak and challenge." Maria paused for a long time. She looked out the window into the deepening spring evening.

"You have experienced loss, too, Maria," Anna said softly.

"Yes. But I have come to see that life gives us obstacles. We must learn to accept them as gifts that help us grow, change, and become even stronger. When one keeps the larger purpose, the mission in life, at the forefront, there is no obstacle too great and no heartbreak that can't be endured. Now, can you tell me more about the ideas that you and your father hold so dear?"

"Oh, yes," said Anna. "They are based on the educator Johann Heinrich Pestalozzi and his student, Friedrich Froebel."

"I know of them, of course. I am interested to know what part of their philosophy you emphasize, or would like to emphasize," said Maria.

"My father started a kindergarten, based on Froebel, for poor children. He was so dedicated to it that it was in our own home. That was when my mother began to object."

"I can't say that I blame her entirely. The idea of having a kindergarten here, in this apartment, with my father . . ." Maria swept her hands in the air to indicate the impossibility. The two women laughed.

"Yes, my mother had a point," said Anna. "But Pestalozzi was dedicated to helping improve the lot of the poor through education. He believed in the whole child, taking into account the family, physical education and activity, as well as the intellectual. He also believed strongly in introducing the right materials for study at the right time in development. He broke the idea of education down into elements, or specific steps, with intellectual and physical concepts attached to each one."

Maria could see Anna warming to her subject, and she encouraged her to continue.

"Froebel created the idea of a kindergarten, or a year for young children to experience these steps along with games, stories, and activities specifically created for their age and development. No one had ever heard of anything like this, and it was terribly difficult to convince parents to allow their children to come. Italian education has not adopted this in any way, although there are thousands of kindergartens in Germany. This is what my father wanted to do. This is what I would like to do."

The two women sat for hours discussing education, Maria's

work with patients, and the state of reform in Italy. Maria hadn't felt like this since her initial conversations with Giuseppe. Finally they heard the clock in the hallway strike midnight.

Renilde came in wearing a nightdress. She suggested they make up a bed for Anna, as it was too late to be out. The three women prepared the sofa together, fitting the linen sheets over the cushions. Maria lowered the window shades and placed a soft blanket over Anna. Turning down the lights, she said, "Our journey has just begun. I have many ideas to discuss with you. But first, you need your rest."

Anna Maccheroni slept soundly. She couldn't remember a time when she had awakened feeling so alive, so positive.

Maria and Renilde served her breakfast. Anna could tell by the books and correspondence on the table that Maria had already been up for hours.

"Good morning," Maria said. "Did you sleep well?"

"Yes, thank you," Anna said.

"We will find a cab for you, so you can get home safely. I hope your father won't think we've kidnapped you." Maria smiled warmly at Anna. "You will hear from me. You are no longer alone."

Chapter Seven

THE SOUL OF A REFORMER

By 1906, the city of Rome, which had been steadily increasing in population, was in a reform-minded phase. The economic boom of the 1880s had been followed by the bust of the 1890s. Those who came to the city in search of better lives found a new kind of misery. Romans had a desire to confront the poverty, illiteracy, and crime in their midst.

The San Lorenzo district was just outside the old Roman wall. It was between the wall and a cemetery, at the terminus of the train station. Several large apartment buildings five stories high, with capacious rooms, had been built there speculatively during the 1890s. When wealthier residents failed to material-ize, the apartments sat vacant and were eventually taken over by squatters. The entire neighborhood became a cesspool of prosti-tution, drugs, and blight.

In 1905, chastened by newspaper articles decrying life in the San Lorenzo, city officials decided to do something. The Roman Association for Good Building, headed by Edoardo Talamo, was given a directive to buy the buildings, clean them up, paint them, provide fountains and courtyards, and rent them. By 1906, a neighborhood that had once been a den of vice was marginally better.

Edoardo Talamo and his associates made sure that renters were gainfully employed. The apartments were subdivided and filled with workers and their families. Men and women worked in the nearby rail yard or factories that dotted the perimeter of the city. Many had to leave their children alone while they worked. Unsupervised, the children began writing on the clean walls, defacing property, pulling out newly planted trees, and causing chaos.

Talamo knew about Maria Montessori, as did many Romans, from her lectures and from the articles that had appeared about her work. He felt that he deserved recognition for the San Lorenzo housing turnaround. But first, he had a problem to solve: the children. He decided to visit Montessori and hear what she had to say.

The Maria Montessori that Talamo met was no longer a young woman beginning her career. She was thirty-six years old. She had an established reputation throughout Italy and Europe. The city of Rome was large, and its population was growing, but the politicians, civic leaders, and those in the upper echelons of Roman social life all knew of her. Her reputation as a physician, a scientist, a popular teacher and lecturer, and a feminist was unparalleled. She had also begun to specialize in diseases of the young.

She held a unique position in the minds of those in power. There was no one else quite like Maria Montessori.

~

In her private life, Maria continued to make regular visits to Mario. He remained with the loving farm family an hour by train from Rome. With his father's dark hair and his mother's pale skin and expressive eyes, he was a beautiful child.

Maria brought him books and some of the educational apparatus, such as building blocks, that she had begun to use with patients. But most of all, they took long walks in the fields surrounding the farm.

Mario knew her as Auntie. He was always happy to see her, although as he grew older there were times when he seemed confused by her presence.

One summer day, Maria and Mario came upon a chrysalis hanging from a branch. "That is a protective shell out of which a butterfly will grow," Maria said, recalling a day in Ancona long ago.

"Is the shell like the butterfly's mother?" Mario asked.

"That is exactly right," answered Maria. "The shell is like a mother protecting her child."

"Why don't I have a mother protecting me?" Mario wanted to know. He asked the question in the matter-of-fact way children sometimes do.

Maria thought her heart would break. She knelt down in front of Mario and put her arms around him. Her eyes filled with tears. She managed, through force of will, to keep them from falling.

"God is protecting all of us," she said. "God is protecting you. We can't always understand the mysteries of life. But you must believe that you do have a mother who loves you very much."

Mario looked into her eyes and said simply, "Yes, Auntie. I do believe."

It was harder than ever that evening to say good-bye. Maria allowed herself to cry on the train going back to Rome. She faced the window so none of the other passengers could see.

As they reached the outskirts of Rome, they passed through the slums of the San Lorenzo. Maria saw young children playing around smoldering garbage near the tracks. Some threw stones at the train. When the train stopped to let off passengers, Maria watched the scene with a combination of dismay and professional interest.

One thin little girl wore a filthy gray rag. Her eyes met Maria's. She pointed to her mouth and rubbed her belly. Maria sat back as the train started up and resolved, again, to spend her life relieving the misery of children like these. It was time for action. There was so much hunger in the world. Hunger for food, for education, for housing, for dignity.

The next day, Edoardo Talamo paid another visit to Maria. He was a thin wisp of a man with a tiny mustache. His hair was slicked back with brilliantine, and he wore light gray gloves that he nervously smoothed and re-smoothed.

"I will get right to the point. I am a busy, busy, man."

"So you have told me on several previous visits," said Maria, stifling a smile.

"I am the head of housing in the San Lorenzo," he said with a huff. "It is a very important position, and I've made tremendous progress. But these little monsters are ruining the buildings. Defacing them. They are inhuman little beasts, and they will ruin my reputation if they are allowed to continue. I need you to suggest someone who can run a daycare and keep them cooped up so my buildings will stay intact while their parents work to make the rent."

"I don't see them, or refer to them, as beasts," said Maria. "They are simply unsupervised children, many of them hungry. Hungry for food, and for education." She was thinking of the girl she had seen from the train.

"I don't care what they are called. I just want it stopped," said Talamo.

"I do have a person in mind."

"Thank God. Who is the poor unfortunate?"

"Me," answered Maria.

Talamo's eyes widened and he nearly sputtered. "You? Surely you are joking! I came to you hoping you could recommend a nursemaid or farm girl with a whip to tame these monsters. Not an educated person, a doctor, a person of science. Not a person of great repute, like myself," he sniffed.

Maria stifled a laugh and then grew very serious, "Please hear me when I say this, Signore Talamo. Educating children is the most important thing anyone can do. They are our future, our hope."

"If I seriously thought any of those children were my hope or my future, I would jump into the Tiber and end it all," he said.

"That won't be necessary. If you will give me complete charge, I will take responsibility for these children. I will start a school for them."

"Well, then," said Talamo, smoothing his gloves a final time. "May God be with you."

"He already is," said Maria, grinning.

◞

On January 6, 1907, Maria woke with a start at five o'clock in the morning. It was the day of Epiphany, when the wise men brought gifts to the baby Jesus. A perfect day to begin a new journey in life. Today Casa dei Bambini, or Children's House, would welcome its first students.

Maria could hear the slow, steady footsteps of her father as he made his way around the kitchen preparing his morning coffee. Alessandro Montessori's life in the military had inculcated the habit of early rising, as well as stoically accepting life as it came. But even this training couldn't hide the disappointment on his face when Maria told him about her new position as the head of a small, one-room classroom for children in the slums of the San Lorenzo.

"I have learned not to question," he said, shaking his head. "I love you. I don't always understand you. But I will always respect you."

"Thank you, Papà," Maria said.

Alessandro's hair was almost completely white now, and he walked with a slight limp. She knew that her choices were often baffling and difficult for him. Even Renilde had hesitated, ever so slightly, when her daughter broke the news. Maria was almost thirty-seven and had given up the income and stability of a medical practice. But Renilde, like Alessandro, accepted Maria's decision with as much equanimity as she could muster.

Other friends and colleagues were not so agreeable.

"A glorified nursemaid?" Professor Sergi protested. "I will tenure you here at the university. Anything but see you wrangle children in the middle of a slum!"

Professor Baccelli was incredulous. "All the years I have known you, all that you have come through, and you are giving your time away? Like this?"

Maria knew the first weeks at Casa dei Bambini would be extremely busy. She went to visit Mario during the week after New Year. The words of her colleagues rang in her ears. Then she saw Mario, who was busy forming sentences and words with small letters she had cut out for him. They spent a happy afternoon together, mother and child, writing and laughing.

When the train stopped at the San Lorenzo station on the way back, Maria realized that the children she was seeing might be her students. She remained convinced there was no more important work than that she was about to do.

A wet sleet fell as Maria made her way to the San Lorenzo. The day would begin with a highly publicized opening ceremony. Maria knew the reason was so politicians like Edoardo Talamo could show off and reassure the public they were "taking care of the slums." Getting Maria Montessori to head the new school was a feather in his cap. He made sure journalists and photographers would be there to record the event.

Casa dei Bambini, at 58 Via dei Marsi, was a single room on the bottom floor of a five-story apartment building. The walls, at Maria's direction, had been freshly whitewashed. There were two long tables covered with bright tablecloths, and three wooden cupboards that held materials Maria had purchased or made herself. There was little money for anything else. Maria had bought an inexpensive copy of a painting, Raphael's "Madonna della Seggiola." To her, it represented both real and idealized versions of motherhood. It symbolized the importance of the caregiver and protector. She hung it on a wall.

Talamo's Roman Association for Good Building paid for just one other employee. There was no money for materials or meals. Maria decided to hire her associate from the neighborhood. She wanted someone who knew the San Lorenzo, who lived there, and who was known to the people. She also wanted someone who was not already trained as a teacher. She reasoned that a trained teacher would be mired in the old rote systems.

Maria hired Candida Nuccitelli, a janitor's daughter. She had grown up in the San Lorenzo and was familiar with many of its residents. Candida was a strong, stocky young woman with a lively sense of humor. She seemed to understand Maria's revolutionary concept. She was not there to teach, direct, or set up activities for the children in the usual way. She was there to facilitate what the children chose to do.

Prior to the first day, Maria posted circulars to be read by all the families sending children to Casa dei Bambini. The rules were simple. The children were to be brought on time. They were to be clean. They were to bring clean aprons to wear over their clothes. In Maria's mind, school was a kind of children's work, to be taken very seriously, and the apron symbolized a uniform, a way of separating the world of the outside from the world of school. Because many of the parents were illiterate, one of Candida's first jobs was to scour the neighborhood, find parents of young children, tell them about the school and explain the rules.

Parents had to commit to a bimonthly meeting with the director to discuss their child's progress and agree on what could be done at home to support their work at school. Children who were continually disruptive would be asked to leave.

Maria reached the building shortly before eight o'clock on the morning of the first day. There was already a line of parents and children outside the door. Several reporters faced the crowd, waiting for something to happen.

Candida Nuccitelli waited inside. She seemed both excited and nervous. Maria was filled with a sense of possibility. Raphael's "Madonna" gazed across the room, and Maria felt the presence of God. She had never been so filled with purpose.

Edoardo Talamo burst in. "Good day, Dr. Montessori! There are reporters here to write about the opening, and then we all have other places to be. So please, let these ragamuffins and their parents in. Make a speech, say a prayer, and let's get this thing going. I am a very busy man!"

Maria calmly replied, "This is not your opening. Casa dei Bambini operates on its own schedule. We are here to serve the children, not the administrators. Our opening will begin in half an hour, as the circular said."

Talamo stamped his foot in annoyance. Maria took no notice. She remained serene and in charge. "Perhaps you would like to look at some of the materials I have made for the children while you wait."

"Buying toys is not part of the budget," Talamo said with alarm.

"The materials are not toys. They are educational apparatus. They are based on years of study of past educational theorists, combined with the practical theories I have developed in my own years of working with patients. I have made them and paid for them myself."

Talamo had no response. He found a mirror and preened in front of it, readying himself for the photographers.

Because of the cold and the sleet, Maria opened the door and invited the families inside. The adults came in slowly and looked around cautiously. Some had never been inside a schoolroom before. For those who had, this was not like any schoolroom they had seen.

The children clung to their parents' legs. Some sniffled. One little girl cried openly, mucous running in rivulets from her nostrils to her lips. Maria knelt down before her, showing her how she wiped her own nose. Then she took out a clean handkerchief and offered it to the girl. The mother reached for it. Maria shook her head and indicated silently that the child should take it. The girl carefully unfolded the handkerchief and wiped her nose.

Maria stood up and smiled. "It takes time to teach them to do things for themselves. But it is worth it in the end." The girl demonstrated wiping her own nose again, this time with pride. Several children clapped.

There were fifty children in all, ranging in age from two to seven. The parents had followed Maria's circular, and the children's clothing appeared to be clean. Many items had clearly been made from old material or put together from siblings' clothing. Most were threadbare and thin. Some had gaping holes. Few children were dressed warmly enough for the cold day. They had all brought aprons of various sizes and shapes. All were clean, and soon they hung neatly on nails.

At precisely 8:30, Talamo stepped to the front of the room and declared, "As a representative of the greatest city in the greatest country in the word, I know this school will be very great, very important, and you will all behave for the glory of Rome!" He indicated that photographers should take his picture. Some did.

Then Maria stepped to the front. There was a perceptible change in the air. The whole room seemed to lean forward, and reporters jostled their way closer. They didn't want to miss a word. Bulbs flashed.

"This is a momentous day indeed," Maria said. "What we are beginning here is going to have reverberations around the world. We are participating, all of us, in an experiment that is going to change the way people everywhere perceive education.

"We are going to create, in the smallest child at the earliest part of development, the ability to choose, to know themselves, to understand what motivates them, what interests them, and to pursue it. Isn't this the most holy part of being human? The ability to choose and be free and independent in our thinking and behavior? To be able to think for ourselves and reach our highest potential?

"This is what we are beginning today. I thank you, the parents, for the courage you have displayed in bringing your precious children here and placing them in our care. History will note what we are starting here today. At Casa dei Bambini, the child is the center of our life. This is truly the children's home: a home for the heart, the mind, the body, and the soul."

There was a respectful silence. Then Talamo stepped up again. The press surrounded Maria and ignored him. He left in a huff. No one seemed to notice his departure.

Anna Maccheroni and another enthusiastic follower, Anna Fedeli, had been invited to the opening ceremony. They were both thrilled and inspired. The way the classroom had been set up and Maria's opening statement reflected all the hopes and dreams they had for a new way of approaching education.

Once the crowd had dispersed and parents had gone to their factory jobs, it was time for the real experiment to begin.

The children lined up at two washbasins. Maria and Candida Nuccitelli showed them how to wash and dry their hands.

Maria had developed a measuring machine that efficiently weighed them and measured their height, the circumference of their heads, wrists, and waists, and the length of their limbs. All of these measurements, plus any specific physical characteristics, were noted on blue note cards.

Children who were not being examined were encouraged to open the cabinets and take out materials. Some hung fearfully at the edge of the room. But as the morning wore on, even the most shy began to watch, if not fully participate, in the activities of their peers.

The rules were simple. Children were allowed to take any set of materials to work with and keep it as long as they liked. They were expected to handle the materials with care. They had to return them to the exact place they found them when they were done. Loud children were encouraged to speak in quiet voices.

Before lunchtime, the children were given small pieces of cloth and asked to clean the areas where they had been working. Several children were given brooms and dustpans. Maria and Candida demonstrated how to use them.

At lunchtime, Candida filled six glass pitchers with water. She indicated that she needed six children to take the pitchers to the tables. Maria said simply, "If you run, they will spill." Six small volunteers carried the pitchers to the tables without spilling a drop. In a similar manner, the children set the tables with fifty glass plates and cups. This took much longer than if the adults had done it themselves. But the children glowed with the pride of accomplishment. They sat down to eat the meager lunches their parents had provided.

Lunch was followed by physical activities, such as marching and moving to rhythms. Then came the ritual of hand-washing and choosing materials to work with.

There were smooth blocks and cylinders that fit into graduated holes, fabrics with hooks and buttons, fabrics of different colors and textures to feel and match, boards with letters to fit correctly, graduated strips of color to put into order, and lacing boards. Many children completed a task, undid what they had done, and started over. Some did this again and again. Maria took careful notes on these behaviors. She timed them to see how long individual children stayed at their tasks.

This was the work of the children. By the end of the first day, after they had cleaned their workplaces, helped sweep the floor, and hung their aprons, Maria felt triumphant. She had taken hundreds of notes that she was eager to aggregate.

Francina had laced and unlaced the ties on the lacing board. Paulo had built an entire tower out of the graduated blocks, after figuring out how they fit together. It had taken him most of the morning, but he stayed at his work with ferocious focus. Antonio had laid out the counting sticks in multiples of two, then four, then eight.

Maria had many ideas about new materials to create and supply to the students. This would take funding. She had ideas for that as well.

She had also noted that it was physically difficult for the children to reach the shelves, cupboards, and long tables. All had originally been built for adults. After the last child had left for the day, Maria pushed one of the chairs and realized how hard it was to move. She wondered aloud, "Why not build child-size tables, chairs, cupboards, and washstands so the children can reach them and move them by themselves? Why not make them out of lightweight wood and paint them bright colors so children are attracted to them and can manipulate them on their own?"

Candida nodded in agreement and stated, in her eminently practical way, "That is a brilliant idea, Maria. And why not have money rain down from the sky to pay for all of this new furniture? You know Talamo won't give you a penny. And you have already spent much of your own money to create the materials the children used today."

"You are right," Maria agreed. "But there were women at the opening today who are dignitaries, women of wealth and means. They want to reform education, just as I do. I am going to ask them for money to fund the new furniture and more materials."

She glanced around the room and smiled. "Today is one of the happiest days of my life. All of my life so far has led up to this. We are starting a revolution!"

"I don't know about revolutions," said Candida. "I am only a janitor's daughter. But I do know that I have never met anyone like you."

"Before long, Montessori schools will be attended by janitors' daughters as well as children of royalty," Maria declared. "I have no doubt of it. I thank you for everything you have done today, Candida. Rest well. We have much more work to do."

As Maria made her way home that night, she was no longer saddened by the signs of poverty around her. "Where there is education, there is hope," she thought. "Today is the culmination of everything I have learned thus far. I can feel it." Entering a wealthier section of Rome, she saw well-dressed people strolling the wide boulevards. She saw people dining at restaurants with white linen tablecloths. She vowed to harness the power of the wealthy to improve the lives of the poor.

Renilde and Alessandro Montessori had not seen their

daughter so happy in a long time. At dinner that evening, Maria regaled her parents with the details of the day: the officiousness of Edoardo Talamo, the shy and fearful looks of the children that turned into focused work, for some, by day's end.

"There was little Paulina, who sat against the wall almost the entire day peering out at us under thick bangs," Maria said excitedly. "She couldn't resist the cylinder blocks and finally came out of her shell to put them in and take them out at least forty times. I counted! Children want to work. They want to be productive. They are capable of so much if we adults just get out of the way." She wound her mother's pasta marinara on her spoon.

"Please explain 'get out of the way'," her father said. "Won't chaos ensue if adults in a classroom allow children to run amok, doing whatever they like? Where does discipline come in?"

"Papà, surely you can understand, being from the military, that eventually what they want to teach soldiers is internal self-discipline. Being able to do for oneself and take responsibility, to make sound decisions in difficult situations based on ethics and self-determination. Surely you would agree that is ultimately for the good of all."

Between bites, she continued. "I want you both to come and visit. Then you will see what I mean. Chaos has no place in my plan for education. On the contrary, I believe a calm, ordered atmosphere is the only answer. You have always provided that for me, and that was my first lesson in life. Many of the families in the San Lorenzo don't even know how to follow the first principles of hygiene. They don't sit down to meals or know how to clean a room.

"The first order in making humans free and independent is to make them capable of caring for their own body and environment. That is the basis for everything. That is why I call my school Casa dei Bambini. It is a home for the children, and we do everything there that would happen at home, with the eye toward mind, spirit, and body. This is the first step along the path of my revolution in education. The next steps are the freedom of choice and self-determination."

"Garibaldi taught me that revolutions can be messy and dangerous," Alessandro said.

"Revolutions are also expensive," Renilde added, with a rueful laugh. "It is time for us to start writing letters to all the wealthy people we know who might want to pay for the furniture and materials you need."

Maria looked lovingly at her parents. They had both grown older. Alessandro's knee, injured in a long-ago battle, was giving him constant pain. Renilde had deep lines around her eyes and mouth. Her shoulders were stooped.

Maria hoped she had given them pride and joy. She knew her decisions had caused consternation at times, and she was sorry for this. "Life is not always easy for those who want to challenge the status quo," she thought. "Not for them. Or for their families."

The Montessoris spent the rest of the evening bent over their dining room table, writing letters to everyone they knew, asking for financial help for Casa dei Bambini. By week's end, money began to trickle in. Maria went to a carpenter in the neighborhood with designs for child-size tables, chairs, cupboards, and shelves.

At Maria's orders, the carpenter also crafted wooden frames, geometric cutouts that fit into wooden boards, wooden rods of different lengths, and cylinders of various circumferences. These would prove to be much more sturdy and lasting than the cardboard cutouts she was now using. Everything was made to Maria's exacting specifications and painted cheerful primary colors.

Maria spent every day at Casa dei Bambini, observing the behavior of the children and their interactions with the materials and each other. She wrote down all the data and studied it in the evenings. She made constant refinements based on what she learned.

The schedule for the day rarely varied. The first hour was for hygiene, measurements, and greetings. The morning was spent on intellectual exercises, gymnastics, and movement. The children were free to do what interested them. Lunch was set, served, and cleaned up by the children.

The afternoon was spent with individual work, games for those who wanted to participate, and eventually writing and reading for those who were ready and who chose to take part. The latter part of the afternoon was taken up with music and time spent outside in the courtyard. The day ended with the children cleaning the entire space and washing themselves in preparation for going home.

Within this framework, all the children were allowed, during most of the day, to choose the materials they wanted to interact with. Maria had designed them to be self-correcting. A cylinder of a certain size could only fit into the corresponding hole in one way. Any child could use any material for as long as they wanted. Interruptions were not allowed. Maria knew that periods of deep focus, and times when a child repeated the same movement or series of movements, were crucial to their development.

Casa dei Bambini was, in Maria's mind, a sacred place where children could do the essential work of developing and growing in a protected environment.

Maria continued to combine her own ideas with ones she gleaned from Itard and Seguin about creating materials and activities that matched the developmental needs of the child. Some of the activities were simply things people do every day: washing oneself, dusting, sweeping, wiping tables, setting tables, washing dishes. During the first days at Casa dei Bambini, Maria noticed children following Candida Nuccitelli to the cupboards. She realized they wanted to participate fully in all aspects of the life of the school. She made the upkeep of the environment and the preparation of meals part of the curriculum.

Once the carpenter finished building wooden frames, Maria stretched large pieces of fabric on some of them. There was a buttoning frame, a lacing frame, a hook-and-eye frame, and a shoe-tying frame. She drew chalk lines on the floor and created balancing games for the children, based on her observations of vestibular development. She made the games increasingly difficult, having the children wear blindfolds, carry glasses of water without spilling them, hold bells without making them ring, and so forth. The games were fun but also developed balance and the pincer movement in the fingers and hands, a precursor to writing. Maria believed fervently in developing the musculature that would allow the child to eventually write, walk, run and perform the practical actions of everyday life.

Maria had long worked with mentally challenged patients at the Orthophrenic School, and as a student, with the notion of letters. Based again on her study of Itard and Seguin, she had created large metal letters for the alphabet. Patients could hold them, trace them, and put them together to form words. Maria was determined to make similar letters for Casa dei Bambini, but she didn't have the funds to hire a metal worker.

One night during the first weeks of Casa dei Bambini, Anna Maccheroni was with Maria in the Montessoris' home. They were going over notes Anna had taken from that day. She and Anna Fedeli had become indispensable assistants to Maria as she struggled to keep up with the endless requests for lectures and letters of inquiry from all over the world.

"I can't find a way to make these letters from metal, to replicate what I had at the Orthophrenic School," Maria said. "They are too expensive and difficult to manufacture. But the children need them."

Stacks of paper sat on the table: notecards, letters, newspapers. There were cardboard boxes that held materials Maria had gathered to take to Casa dei Bambini, and sandpaper she had used to smooth pieces of wood. Anna Maccheroni took one of the box lids and traced the letter A. She cut it out and held it aloft. It was about six inches high. She traced the A on sandpaper, cut it out, and glued it to the front of the letter she had cut from the box lid, rough side out. The final letter was light, sturdy, and easy to manipulate. "Now imagine it painted a bright color," Anna said.

"This is a genius solution. Why didn't I think of it?" Maria asked.

"Because you have thought of everything else," Anna said, laughing. "I was inspired by you."

Joined by Renilde, the women sat for hours making alphabets of letters. Then they painted them and left them out to dry. The next morning, Maria took them to Casa dei Bambini. The children were entranced by them. Maria invented tracing games and touching games, where the children guessed letters and their sounds while blindfolded. This stimulated their tactile senses and got them ready for reading and writing.

Newspaper articles accompanied by photographs of Maria and the children began to appear. Most mentioned Edoardo Talamo only briefly, if at all. Following the interests of their readers, journalists reported on events at Casa dei Bambini. They explored the personality and the theory behind the success of the school. Talamo was not pleased at being cut out of the publicity. He insisted on making a visit to the school during its third week. He brought along the minister of education. The minister was deeply impressed.

A month after the opening of Casa dei Bambini, Maria's parents visited for the first time. It happened to be the same day the new furniture arrived. It was unseasonably warm for early February. Four carts pulled up in front of the school. They were loaded with the brightly-colored furniture, piled up like large gumdrops. The chairs and tables stood out against the dirty gray buildings of the neighborhood.

Neighbors peered out their windows at the sight. Some came down to the street and offered to help unload. Maria thanked them, then asked them to please leave the furniture near the front door. They stood back as children came out, carefully picked up the chairs, which were light enough for even a three-year-old to manage, and carried them into the classroom. When all the furniture was indoors and everything was in its proper place, Maria, the children, and the neighbors stood back and admired the cheerful, inviting room.

Renilde and Alessandro Montessori entered a classroom full

of color and life. Several children greeted them and led them to new chairs. Then they went back to their work. Renilde and Alessandro saw children everywhere. They were astounded by the calmness that filled the room. They had expected a loud playground, but Casa dei Bambini was a serious workplace.

Some children sat on small pieces of carpet, putting wooden geometric shapes into corresponding cutout pieces of wood. Two girls were placing wooden rods in multiples of two in neat columns. Three very small girls were blindfolded and were touching the sandpaper sides of cutout alphabet letters, guessing which ones they were.

Maria was helping a pale, dark-haired boy plant a seed in a pot of dirt. It would join other plants in various stages of growth that stood on a shelf beside them. Renilde noted Maria's care and mother's touch. Her heart was full of love for a daughter who, unable to raise her own son, was creating hope and a better life for all of these children.

Renilde walked over to where Maria was sitting with the child. She heard him ask, "Am I your favorite?"

"You are all my favorite," Maria replied. "All children are my favorite." She looked up at her mother and smiled. Both women thought of Mario.

Renilde returned to her small stool beside her husband. She put her arm through his and they sat together, gazing around the room. Fifty children sat, stood, walked, and worked with focus and intention. All seemed to be consciously engaged in what Alessandro and Renilde could now see was children's work. They understood what Maria had been saying when she used that language. This school was proof of everything she had been telling them.

They watched Maria conduct an experiment with the

children. A four-year-old girl named Pepina sat on a canary yellow chair with a small board and five cylinders of different lengths and circumferences. She was fitting them into the correct holes, then taking them out, mixing them up and starting over again. Maria and the other children formed a circle around her and began marching. Pepina was so focused she didn't look up. Maria and the children picked up the chair with Pepina in it. She remained focused.

Later, over dinner, the Montessoris talked about the day.

"If you had told us about Pepina, we would not have believed you," Alessandro said. "We had to see it with our own eyes."

"What you saw was the capability, the depth, and the potential of a child," Maria said. "One day, the same level of focus in an adult might find the key to eradicating a disease or creating a peace treaty. This is the heart of our work at Casa dei Bambini."

"Seeing is understanding. You have created internal discipline. I saw it in the children and felt it in the room. Everything you have been saying is true."

"It is the greatest gift you can bestow on a human being," said Renilde.

"I can't bestow it," said Maria. "It can only come from the individual when the environment is set up to encourage it and protect it. This is my life's work. I know it now."

A few days later, it was so warm the windows of the schoolroom were open. Pepina's mother sat outside with a sleeping infant in her arms. Maria saw a teaching moment. She asked Pepina's mother if she could hold the child. The mother carefully passed the infant through the open window to Maria.

Maria walked to the center of the room, cradling the child, still sleeping soundly. The children stopped their work and watched.

"See how peaceful and quiet this child is?" Maria asked. Her voice fell to a near-whisper. "I'll bet you can't be as quiet or as still." The children gathered around Maria and the baby.

"His peaceful, beautiful presence informs us all," Maria said. Even the busiest, noisiest children in the room stopped what they were doing. Finally there was no sound in the room whatsoever.

"See if your ears can hear her sweet breathing," Maria murmured. In the distance, a church bell could be heard. A horse-drawn cart rolled down the brick street and the driver said "Whoa!" But no sound came from the schoolroom. Fifty children, two adults, and an infant formed circle of composure and peace. The children remained still as Maria got up, walked to the window, and returned the child to her mother.

Maria returned to the circle. "You have given yourselves the gift of silence," she said. "You have experienced the freedom and knowledge that comes from being silent, from beginning to listen to and understand the voice within. This is your soul. Cherish it. Listen to it. Learn from it."

The silence exercise became a vital part of each day at Casa dei Bambini. The children looked forward to it.

Maria had developed materials for tactile and cognitive work. Some materials strengthened the muscles in the hands, wrists, and fingers in preparation for writing. But she thought it was too soon to teach writing to most of her students, or reading. Then she noticed that some children were starting to put letters together on their own. One day in late February, Maria was sitting with a group of children on the small patio outside the classroom, near the chimney for the building. They were working with large letter cutouts. Maria put together the letters that spelled chimney.

Five-year-old Antonio started tracing them and speaking their sounds. Suddenly he blurted out "Chimney!" He pointed from the letters to the chimney and back to the letters again. "Chimney! Chimney! Chimney!" he said, his voice rising. The other children surrounded him gleefully, as though they understood the leap he had made. They began to clap and cheer.

Antonio took four more letters and spelled "wall" against the patio wall. He took another four and spelled "tree" on the ground before a spindly tree. He was wild with excitement. "I can read! I can read!" he exclaimed, jumping up and down with joy. "No one in my family can read. My Mamma and Papà will be so proud. I can read!"

Maria wiped tears of happiness from her eyes. Last week, when she visited Mario, he read aloud to her. She didn't know exactly how or when he began to read. She missed that moment with her own son. But she had been able to facilitate it for Antonio, a boy from the San Lorenzo whose own parents were illiterate. His life would be full of new possibilities.

Journalists, reformers, wealthy socialites, and educators began to visit Casa dei Bambini. From the first day, because of Maria Montessori's reputation, people were fascinated by this radical experiment in education and social reform. Was it the harbinger of permanent change? There were days when it seemed the crowd of visitors equaled or surpassed the number of students.

Turning the corner onto Via dei Marsi, visitors were struck by the gray buildings, the barking of dogs, the smells of sewage, and the sense of grinding poverty. On reaching Casa dei Bambini, they were greeted politely by children who seemed barely out of infancy. Maria was gracious to everyone, but there was a strict rule against talking to the children or interrupting them at their work.

Visitors were treated to a room full of brightly colored furniture. They saw shelves stacked neatly with what Maria called her apparatus; the materials she developed that were the basis for the children's work. One table held a colorful glass vase with a fresh flower. A shelf was crowded with potted plants in various stages of growth. There were hooks for children to hang their aprons. The room had a sense of ordered calm, warmth, and safety, in stark contrast to the world outside. Sunshine and natural light poured in from three windows that had been cut into the walls. Raphael's "Madonna" watched over the space with benevolence and grace.

The most impressive part of the visit was always the children themselves. Visitors were astonished to see so many children intently focused on their tasks. Many worked individually, sitting on small pieces of carpet on the floor, or at tables. Some sat with wooden blocks or sticks in their laps, counting, stacking, or working and reworking puzzles. The room was like a busy beehive. There was a constant hum of activity, and each person seemed to know exactly where to go and what to do. The children were content and self-directed.

Visitors came expecting to see a traditional schoolroom with metal desks or long benches. They looked in vain for the grim-faced teacher of their own past experience, droning away at the front of the room. They could find not one bored, distracted face among the children. The contrast between what most visitors had experienced as children was profound. For educators forced to teach in the old ways, Casa dei Bambini was a revelation.

On a bright Monday morning in early April, Candida Nuccitelli came to Maria, who was laying out word cards for a group of children. "Miss Maria," she stammered, "there is a visitor at the door. It is the queen! Queen Margherita!"

"Don't keep her waiting," Maria said calmly. "Children, shall we welcome the Queen?" She knew that any visitor, royalty or commoner, would see exactly the same school, the same focused children connected deeply to their work. She was not at all fazed.

Two of the children, Rafaela and Antonio, greeted the queen. The mother of King Victor Emmanuel III, she was a tall, stately, handsome woman, known for her interest in reform and the lives of impoverished children. She seemed to understand immediately the sense of the school and insisted on sitting in a corner on a small chair, unobtrusively watching the children. She stayed for most of the day and was charmed by their maturity and sense of responsibility.

At lunchtime, two boys carried a small table, sat it in front of her, and served her a bowl of hot soup. She watched three four-year-old girls begin the rudiments of writing by tracing the outlines of letters. She was astounded to see a young girl of four begin to sound out words. Most of all, she was impressed by the caring relationship between the adults and the children.

At day's end, she stood and approached Maria. She didn't want to disturb the children's work. "I know you are busy now," she said. "We must meet at another time and discuss how I can help you in your work here. You are creating miracles."

"I am not creating miracles, Your Highness," Maria replied. "I am only allowing the children here to find their own miracles. I am grateful for your offer of help. I know it comes from a sincere desire to make their lives better."

"You are creating the foundation for the next generation, who will be the glory of Italy," Margherita said. She left quietly and stepped into a waiting carriage.

A fruit vendor from the neighborhood leaned against the lopsided, splintered wheel of his own rickety cart. He was separating out spoiling fruit and giving it to a line of waiting people. The good fruit would be saved to sell in a wealthier neighborhood.

"Fancy people are coming to visit you, Miss Maria!" he yelled out.

Maria smiled from the doorway of the school. "They want to see the children, not me," she insisted. "They are the reason the school exists."

In late June, Edoardo Talamo and a colleague in the education ministry paid a surprise visit to Casa dei Bambini. Talamo had been reading endless articles about Maria and hearing positive reports. He was angry that all the publicity gave credit to Maria and not to him. He felt the stories were overblown and was secretly eager to find fault. Even though the success of the school reflected well on his administration, he was incensed not to be the center of attention. He hoped the visit would catch Maria unaware and give him something to use against her.

The two men came upon a scene of calm, peaceful activity. There was a hum of productivity. Several children were carrying pitchers full of water to fill glasses for the midday meal. Others cleaned their spaces and carefully put away their work. Two came to greet the gentlemen and led them to chairs.

"This far exceeds my expectation," said Roberto DiBenedetto, Edoardo Talamo's colleague. He saw a boy who was tracing letters and asked his age.

"I am Roberto and I am four, sir. Well, almost four!" said the small boy with brown hair and freckles.

"I am Mr. DiBenedetto. I am almost sixty-four. You and I have the same first name, Roberto. Can you spell it for me?"

"Yes, sir, I can!" said the boy. And he did.

"This woman, this Montessori, is a genius," Roberto DiBenedetto said to Edoardo Talamo. "You can see it here. You can feel it."

"Too much money is being spent on things we don't need," Talamo fumed. "Too much money on too few children. Why do we need flowers and plants in a classroom? We aren't teaching gardening!"

Maria had come to stand beside Talamo and DiBenedetto. "It will be interesting to experiment with different children from other populations and neighborhoods. Even other countries," she said.

"What are you talking about?" ask Talamo.

"We will be opening another Montessori school on the Via Solari in Milan, with funds provided by Queen Margherita. There is interest in several more in Rome and possibly one in Switzerland."

Talamo's eyes popped. DiBenedetto shook Maria's hand, congratulating her. Maria could sense Talamo's anger. She understood that the powerful potential of her ideas was threatening to him. Her vision was becoming global. It went beyond the San Lorenzo, beyond Rome, and beyond Italy. "I am grateful, on behalf of these children and their parents, for the opportunity we have been given here," she said. "Now we must make it available to children everywhere."

Talamo bristled. "This is just a nursery school in the San Lorenzo. It is not our mission to change the world."

"But it is my mission," said Maria, "and I intend to accomplish it."

Chapter Eight

THE SOUL OF A TEACHER

"Do you have more stories about Edoardo Talamo?" Mario asked. Maria Montessori laughed heartily. It had become one of their private jokes, a reference to anyone who was difficult. It was 1909, and Mario was eleven years old. Maria was on one of her visits to see him. They walked, as was their treasured habit, on the country road near the home of the family who was raising him. Olive trees flanked them on both sides. The warm March afternoon was turning into a chilly evening, yet neither wanted to go back quite yet.

In a motherly gesture, Maria turned up Mario's collar and said, "You aren't dressed warmly enough."

"I never get cold, Auntie," replied Mario. "I am always warm. It must be something in my genes." He did a little jig to reassure her.

Mario enjoyed Maria's visits and anticipated them eagerly. Maria was astonished by his growth. He seemed wise beyond his years. He was on the verge of becoming a young man.

Mario went back to being serious. "How many schools do you have now?"

Maria was impressed that he was interested. Most boys Mario's age were playing with frogs and skipping stones. She couldn't help thinking it was a sign of intelligence.

"There are two in the San Lorenzo," she answered, "Three are opening in Switzerland, and I am thinking of asking Anna Maccheroni to open the one in Milan. She will be terrified, as she has never lived anywhere but Rome. But I know she can do it. I am so fortunate to have her help. And, of course, my parents. I don't know what I would do without them. The pile of letters and requests for speaking engagements grows every day. I try to keep up, but I am getting more and more behind. Then there is the problem of not enough teachers."

"And all must be trained by you, and only you, in the Montessori way," he said, with emphasis on the final three words. Maria knew he was teasing her.

"I am stubborn about that," she admitted. "But I am the only person who uses a combination of science and psychology. How else can I guarantee quality? How can I be sure that a teacher will focus on the right things? The proof is in the pudding."

"Speaking of pudding," said Mario, rubbing his stomach, "I am starving." He skipped down the road and kicked a rock high in the air. He was still a boy, after all. They approached the cottage where Mario lived with the Fanelli family. Signora Fanelli came to the door and invited Maria to stay for dinner.

"I would love to," said Maria with a sigh, "but I must return to Rome tonight, as I leave tomorrow for Milan, then Switzerland, where I am giving a lecture."

Maria's transportation to the train station had arrived. It was time to go. Maria gazed into the Fanellis' cottage. A crackling fire warded off the late spring chill. She could smell bread being baked and sausages frying in a pan. She wanted nothing more than to step inside, be enveloped by the warmth, and eat dinner with her son.

Mario stepped forward, "Good-bye, Auntie. Thank you for coming."

"I won't see you for several months," said Maria. "I will be traveling."

"I know," said Mario grinning, "Montessori must teach teachers 'the Montessori way.'"

Maria reached down and tousled his hair, which was silky. She kissed his cheek, which was cold and smelled like the woods.

The back of the carriage had an isinglass curtain, and she raised it. Moisture had condensed on the inside. Maria took her finger and wrote "Mario." She imagined her son eating dinner with the Fanellis. He was shoveling food into his mouth and gesturing excitedly. They were laughing at something he was saying. She looked forward to a time when she would no longer have to say good-bye to her son. She was determined to change the system that separated any mother from her child.

Maria left for Milan early the next morning. It was nearly April 1909. As the train sped from Rome to Milan, Maria sifted through piles of letters her mother had packed for her to read along the way. They filled a large briefcase.

There were letters from nearly every country in Europe. Several were from India and China. Nearly half were from America. All expressed a great interest in Montessori schools. Many begged Maria to come and lecture. Others asked that she start a school and lead seminars for people who wanted to become teachers. Still others requested copies of the materials she used. Or they wanted to know how and where they could purchase these materials. Maria worked diligently, but as the train pulled into Milan, she had only made a dent in the pile.

Anna Maccheroni greeted Maria with a bouquet of flowers. It had been an experiment for Anna to open the school in Milan. She and Maria had many talks beforehand, with Maria reassuring Anna that she could do it. "She looks thin as a reed, but happy," Maria thought, accepting the flowers and kissing Anna on the cheek. "Her eyes are sparkling. She carries herself with more confidence."

"I know you must be exhausted from your journey," said Anna breathlessly, "but I can't wait to show you Milan's Casa dei Bambini!"

"I am not too exhausted for that," said Maria.

Anna was animated in a way Maria had never seen. "I have come to know Milan during these months I have been preparing the school," Anna said. "The Sforza Castle is a monument to . . . well, some kind of excess. But the labor union was founded here in Milan. This city is the center of industry. The Sempione Tunnel opened three years ago and is a marvel of engineering. You would find it interesting. And, of course, the 'Last Supper'! I saw it."

They arrived at Casa dei Bambini. The outside looked unprepossessing, except for the door. Anna had painted it bright blue.

She opened the door. It was like stepping from a gray, wintery day into the middle of May. As in Rome, the room was full of brightly colored child-size furniture. The Montessori apparatus, the materials Maria designed and developed, were neatly arrayed on the shelves.

There was something new that Maria saw immediately. It was a series of bells in various sizes. Anna clapped her hands with excitement as she explained how they worked. Each bell had a different tone on the scale and could be used to teach intervals. She had come up with the idea on her own.

Next, Anna pointed toward a door and indicated Maria should open it. They stepped into a tiny but meticulously ordered garden. The area was less than twenty feet square, but a small path had been cleared around the perimeter. There was a vegetable garden in its beginning stages, and an herb garden. In the middle grew a young almond tree.

"You did this?" Maria asked in wonder.

Anna nodded proudly. "A young gentleman from the neighborhood helped me plant the almond tree. He said he didn't believe the children would leave it alone. But I said he was wrong. He has never seen a Montessori child."

Anna was bristling with energy. Maria considered the young woman standing before her. She had come to her almost three years before, lost and depressed. The person standing before her now was full of life and purpose. Maria began to see that their work affected the teachers as well as their students. The potential for change didn't end with childhood.

Opening day for the Casa in Milan dawned bright and promising. White clouds drifted over the Milan cathedral. Its massive Gothic spires reached to the sky. The cathedral was dedicated to St. Mary of the Nativity, a young mother, and Maria reflected on this as she made her way to the school. As on opening day for the first Casa dei Bambini in Rome two years before, parents and children were waiting outside. They looked hesitant and expectant, as all parents do when they are putting their children in someone else's care. Some looked hurried, and Maria understood they were on their way to work.

The parents and children seemed surprised and charmed by what they saw when the door opened. One little girl with long, thick braids ran to pick up a lacing board. Within seconds, she was completely focused on her task.

Maria walked to the center of the room. "You see this young child who has gone to her work," she said to the parents. "Just as your work today might be sewing or cleaning, selling or making things in a factory, her work is to learn the mental and physical skills that will eventually make her a productive, independent human being.

"You have brought your children to me and put your faith in me. I honor that faith. No mother should ever have to worry that while she is working to make a living, her child is not safe. No woman should ever have to make a choice between pursuing her God-given potential and making certain her children are cared for. But this is not just a daycare. This is a place that will help your children reach their full potential. This is a place of spiritual, mental, and physical sustenance.

"While you are out working today, or caring for your home or your other children, the children you leave with us will also be hard at work. The faith you have shown in us will be rewarded. But we can't do this alone. The work we begin must continue in the home, in places where girls and women are valued, in homes where children learn to care for themselves as they respect their parents' ethics and values."

Just then, the little girl with the lacing board laughed out loud. She had completed her work.

"We will also have a great deal of fun," Maria added.

Maria stayed in Milan for several weeks to observe the new school and help Anna, who had worked so hard to open the school that she promptly became ill. Anna had found a Milanese woman with a teaching degree and several years of experience in a regular Italian elementary school. Her name was Lucia. Anna was certain that Lucia understood the Montessori philosophy. Especially with Anna indisposed, Maria agreed to give Lucia a try.

On Lucia's first day, Maria observed a boy who wanted to see what was going on in a crowd of older children. He began pulling a small chair toward the edge of the group so he could stand on it. Lucia stepped in, picked him up and held him high, saying "Now you can see!"

Maria took her aside.

"Were you observing Franco?" Maria asked.

"Oh, yes, and I felt sorry for him," said Lucia. "He wanted to see what was going on and I wanted to help."

"What did you see him doing?" asked Maria. "What exactly did you observe?"

"He was pulling a chair," Lucia answered.

"Why?"

"I suppose so he could step on it and see."

"Was that his idea, his solution?"

"Yes, I believe so," said Lucia.

"And would it have worked, do you think?"

"I . . . why, yes. I think it would have."

"Lucia, you said you felt sorry for Franco. But it matters not what we feel. What matters is what we do. We must never take away children's independence, their sense of solving problems, of finding their own balance. That is true freedom." She paused for a moment before asking, "Do you understand? I know it is very different from the way you have been taught."

"True freedom. Yes. I do understand. Thank you," Lucia said.

After lunch, Maria walked into the school and found Lucia lying on the floor. Her white petticoats were clearly visible, and two children were wrestling with her. One little girl was tickling her. Another was pulling her hair and laughing. When Lucia saw Maria, she smiled and said, "True freedom!"

Maria was horrified. This was a perfect example of what critics of her work feared: that giving children their freedom meant allowing them to do anything they liked.

Maria put her hands gently on the backs of the children, who immediately stopped wrestling. "Can you please bring Lucia a glass of water?" she asked, "Remember, if you run, the water will spill." The two girls walked to the water pump outside and returned with a glass of water, walking slowly and carefully.

Maria knelt beside Lucia, who had now gathered herself and was sitting on a small chair.

"There is no freedom in chaos," Maria began. "Growth and meaningful independence come from order and dignity. Our children are free to explore and free to choose what interests them and what is appropriate for their age and readiness. They are not free to treat us or their peers disrespectfully or inappropriately. To do so, or to allow them to do, is a violation of our most sacred duty to them and to their parents. Do you understand, Lucia?"

"Yes, I think so," Lucia said. But Maria could see she was embarrassed and confused.

"I know you are doing your best. We will continue to learn together, always by observing. It has taken me all of my life to understand what I just told you. And I am still learning every day."

"I want to understand," Lucia said. "I love this place. I believe in what you are doing here. And I know I can learn. Please forgive my ignorance."

"It isn't ignorance, my dear," said Maria. "You are steeped in the old ways of thinking. It takes time and effort to change."

Over the next two weeks, Maria and Lucia shared their lives, their ideas, and new ways of working with children. By the time Anna Maccheroni was well enough to return, Maria was satisfied with Lucia's progress. On the train to Rome, she began planning ways to replicate her teaching process with a large group of potential Montessori teachers.

Renilde Montessori greeted her daughter warmly when she returned from Milan. Knowing she would be tired and hungry, Renilde prepared one of Maria's favorite meals, pasta marinara. Alessandro smoked a pipe as they lingered over a dessert of fig tarts. It was early spring 1909. A slight breeze ruffled the dining room curtains.

With her parents, and especially her mother, Maria could express herself openly about her professional life.

"On some days, I feel I am being torn into pieces," she said. "There are so many things to keep track of. The new schools that are opening. Staffing them with correctly trained teachers. Manufacturing all the materials and making sure they are paid for. Then there are my lectures and my continued teaching at the university.

"Don't get me wrong. I know God has given me a gift. But because the Montessori method is new and not always understood, I feel I have to be there myself to oversee new schools and teachers. A desire to teach in a Montessori school isn't enough. It took me weeks with Lucia, even though no one could have been more willing and eager. I spent nearly twenty years developing these concepts, and I can't expect anyone to understand them in just one day. They also need to understand the underlying principles, the history, and the specificity of how important it is to offer the right thing to each child at the right time. And they need to practice with real children."

"And then there are the letters," said Alessandro, pointing with his pipe to the stacks of mail on the hall table.

"And the presents that have arrived from around the world," said Renilde. "The Americans sent something in a huge box. It was so heavy the postman could barely carry it up the stairs."

"Now you've piqued my curiosity," Maria said.

They opened the box together. It was a beautiful set of linen sheets. Beneath the sheets were several large, heavy bottles of an amber-colored liquid. A note read:

Dear Doctor Maria Montessori,

This gift represents the two sides of my life. The linen sheets are handwoven on our estate in Perugia. The liquor is Kentucky bourbon whiskey that can only be made in the state of Kentucky in my native America.

Thank you for allowing my husband and me to visit Casa dei Bambini. It was enlightening, and I hope to bring Montessori to the schools on our estate in Perugia. I will be in Rome on May 2 and would love to see you. I will come for you at 9 a.m.

Yours truly,
Alice Hallgarten (Baroness Franchetti)

"I am glad we opened this!" Maria exclaimed. "Tomorrow is May 2. Alice is a marvelously clever and lively woman, an American who married an Italian baron."

"I'll put the linens on your bed," said Renilde.

"And I will be very glad to taste test the Kentucky bourbon whiskey from America," said Alessandro.

At precisely nine o'clock the next morning, there was a staccato knock on the door of the Montessori apartment, where they were enjoying a late breakfast. Renilde made her way down the stone steps. A loud voice echoed in the entryway, and Maria heard someone run up the stairs two at a time.

A petite woman with curly blonde hair burst into the room. She wore a tiny braided jacket, cinched at the waist, with a striped navy and white skirt. The blue points of her red collar were tied in a knot. A small flat white hat with a red pompom completed the nautical theme. She strode across the room to hug Maria.

"We only met once before, but I am a hugger," she announced. "You must excuse my terrible Italian, learned by way of an American teacher by way of Philadelphia, or Philly, as we say in the States. I hope you remember me. And I hope you got the gift I sent? And most of all, I hope you aren't teetotalers. Are you?"

She looked around and saw Alessandro's pipe, a small glass, and a bottle of bourbon that had clearly been opened.

"Well, I guess you aren't teetotalers! Happy to know that! Alice Hallgarten of Philly, better known in these parts as Baroness

Franchetti. Do I look like a baroness to you? I am just a little gal from Pennsylvania."

"You look like the best baroness I have ever seen," offered Alessandro.

"I can see where you get your charm, Maria," the baroness said with wink. "Say, what are you eating? It looks delicious." She peered over Maria's shoulder and snatched a piece of bread from a basket. "I have terrible manners, I know, but suddenly I'm as hungry as a bear. And why don't you Italians ever have butter around?"

By now, Maria was laughing uncontrollably. "I don't know which question to answer first, but I will be glad to share my frittata with you."

"You don't have to ask me twice," said the baroness. "Who made it?"

"I did," said Maria. "My mother made the bread."

"You don't say," said the baroness with wonder. "Where are your servants?"

"We don't have servants," Maria replied.

"Now that is what I call impressive," said the baroness with a whistle. "But it sure looks like you could use some help." She pointed to the pile of letters stacked precariously on the hall table. "It looks like you were writing letters over breakfast. That's not good for the digestion. Not that it's any of my business, but I'm guessing most of these letters are from people who want to work with you or learn to become teachers, versed in the Montessori method, right?"

"You have guessed correctly," said Maria. "I hate to disappoint them."

"You don't have to," said the baroness. "That's exactly why I have come today. My husband and I want to offer our estate as the site of your first teacher training course. We will provide everything. We have room for one hundred students, although we would like to send some of the teachers from the schools on our estate so we can establish Montessori schools there. We also have plenty of children at schools on the estate, so you can have a laboratory school during the teacher training course."

Maria's eyes filled with tears of gratitude. "How can I thank you enough? God has sent me to you."

"God by way of your mother," the baroness said. "She wrote me a letter suggesting it, and I can't think of a better idea or use of our blessings. Education for the masses is the only answer. You are lucky to have a mother like Renilde."

"I thank God for her every day," said Maria.

"It's settled then," said the baroness. "August at the Villa Montesca. It's a deal. And let's be clear. This is not for our own profit. Whatever fees the students pay will go to you so you can start more of your wonderful schools. Or hire someone to help you so you don't collapse. Some of the people who wrote those letters are going to be very happy. You don't mind if I take the last bit of bread, do you? It's so good! And Alessandro, in America we toast a deal with a shot of whiskey. What do you say to that?"

Alessandro Montessori nodded his agreement.

Maria woke on July 1, 1909 to a soft knock on her door. It took a moment to realize where she was. She had slept deeply. The room was flooded with sunshine. The ceiling was painted sky blue and trimmed in gold. Through the large arched window she could view the ancient city of Città de Castello.

She was at Villa Montesca, the home of Baron and Baroness

Franchetti. The train trip south to Perugia with Anna Maccheroni, Anna Fedeli, and Elizabeth Ballerini, a new young associate, was just yesterday. But already it seemed like weeks ago. They had left behind the noise and bustle of Rome. They had been welcomed to this magical place with a sumptuous dinner. Maria could not recall a time when she had slept so soundly.

The knock repeated. "Please come in," Maria called. A uniformed servant brought a tray with coffee in a silver urn, a dish of plums and peaches in cream, and a pair of soft-boiled eggs perched on a delicate china pedestal. She slid the tray onto the snow-white linen bedspread.

"Does Signora want her books and notes?" she asked. "The baroness said you might."

Before Maria could reply, her satchel full of work was placed carefully near the bed and the servant wordlessly disappeared.

Maria sat back on her pillows. Her first thought, as it was every day, was of Mario. She said a prayer for him, for her parents, and for blessings on this first teacher training, which would begin the next day. Students were starting to arrive. She could hear the crunch of wheels on gravel and the sounds of different accents and languages.

She said a prayer of gratitude for the Franchettis. She hadn't realized how exhausted she had been until she got on the train. She had visited Mario the day before, and his words to her as she said good-bye were "Don't forget to let people help you, Auntie." He would be happy to see her now.

The next day, Maria gave her opening lecture. As she entered the room, her heart began to pound with excitement. There were flowers everywhere. There were students from France, Germany, England, the Netherlands, Spain, Scotland, and Ireland, and teachers from the schools on the Franchettis' estate. There was a large contingent of students from America. Many had visited Montessori classrooms in Rome and Milan and were eager to know how to start their own schools.

American educator Anne E. George, American author Dorothy Canfield Fisher, and Josephine Tozier, a journalist from the American magazine *McClure's*, all sat in the front row. Each had visited Montessori schools several times. Anne E. George had taught at the Latin School in Chicago and was fascinated by the idea of child-centered learning. Dorothy Canfield Fisher was interested in writing a parenting book based on Maria's theories. Josephine Tozier had been hired by her boss, Samuel Sidney McClure, to cover the first teacher training for his magazine.

Baroness Franchetti introduced Maria. "You aren't interested in seeing or hearing from me," she said. "I just wanted to welcome all of you here. You are going to hear from one of the greatest minds in Europe, or anywhere, for that matter. Listen carefully. You won't be sorry. I am honored to present Maria Montessori."

Maria looked over the audience and began, "We are not here for ourselves, but for children. For the current generations and the ones that will come after us. We are not here to merely become teachers. We are here to understand how to protect, how to facilitate, how to understand the development of children so that we, the adults in their lives, may allow them to reach their greatest potential.

"Freedom is the aim of our work. Freedom for ourselves. Freedom for children to become self-directing and self-motivated, to understand themselves as ethical human beings, part of the race of mankind.

"I am a scientist. One of the most basic jobs of a scientist is to observe. During the next four weeks, I am going to ask you to become observers. I am going to ask you to develop your keenest powers of observation. The object of our attention is going to be the child between ages two and six. We will observe children who are the sons and daughters of the workers on this estate. But I have found that children are alike the world over, whether they come from poverty or privilege. They have developmental stepping-stones that, if nurtured in the right way at the right time, can help them grow into ethical, powerful, whole human beings who can create a better, more peaceful world. A world without war. A world without poverty. With dignity. With hope. With love. There is no other way."

The audience rose to their feet, clapping and cheering. Maria acknowledged their applause with a modest bow of her head.

"Now the real work begins," she said, rolling out a skeleton and a large blackboard. "Let's start right away with the human anatomy. If we have the time today, we will get to the brain." Anna Maccheroni brought out a model of a skull and placed it on a table. "Before we understand the internal, we must try to understand the external."

Four weeks of lectures followed. Maria spoke on subjects that included the physical and psychological development of young children, the philosophy behind the Montessori classroom, and the theoreticians that influenced her. She described the purpose of didactic materials, or apparatus, demonstrating each one and its purpose in the developmental chain. She spoke about the issues that might arise in establishing Montessori schools, given the current state of educational systems in most countries. She spoke without notes and used many examples, telling stories from her own life and her work at the Orthophrenic School to illustrate her points.

The lectures took place in the mornings. During the afternoons, the students observed children and gradually began to practice their skills in an actual classroom set up as a demonstration and teaching laboratory. Maria, as always, taught by doing. She was in the classroom each day after lecturing and answering questions for four hours.

Baroness Franchetti became a sort of mother figure to Maria that summer, even though she was only a few years older than Maria. She constantly spoke to Anna Maccheroni, Anna Fedeli, and Elizabeth Ballerini about the "dottoressa," as Maria had come to be called at Villa Montesca.

"I've never seen anything like it," the baroness said one day. "The woman has more stamina than Teddy Roosevelt. And believe me, that is saying something. She lectures all day, works with her students and the children all afternoon, then studies and reads every night."

Both Annas and Elizabeth laughed knowingly.

"Let's see if we can at least encourage her to rest before dinner," said the baroness. "I'll set up a chaise in the garden outside her room. I'll insist that she rest."

That afternoon, when the last child had left the classroom, the baroness appeared and said, "No arguing. You are going to rest before dinner. The Annas, Elizabeth and myself all insist." Maria gave in. The baroness led her to a chaise next to a gurgling fountain just outside Maria's room.

"I will come and get you in half an hour," the baroness said.

"Yes, Mother. I promise to be good," said Maria with a grin. Ten minutes later, the baroness looked out her bedroom window and saw Maria reading and writing. In moments, she was at Maria's side.

"I've caught you. You are a naughty girl," the baroness said with mock exasperation. "What would you say if your students did this?"

"I would say they are obviously driven to concentrate, and the focus they are giving to the object of their concentration should be honored."

The baroness laughed. "You are a crafty woman, Maria Montessori. And what, pray tell, is the focus of your concentration?"

"Well, first of all, there is the daily letter I write to my nephew," Maria said.

"Your nephew. Yes, of course I know, because we take it every day to town to mail it," said the baroness.

"I have also been writing outlines of the various lectures I have been giving," said Maria. "I don't often use notes. But I want to remember the sequences."

The sun was beginning to set behind the hills overlooking the Villa Montesca. The two women paused for a moment, looking at the purple shadows.

"You should write a book!" the baroness suddenly exclaimed. "I can't believe I just said that. More work! But it seems to me it's all there in your brain already, and it's just a matter of writing it down. The baron and I will handle all the details of publishing. You, of course, will receive any profit made from the sale. We don't need it and we only want to help the world know of the work of Maria Montessori."

"You are truly selfless." said Maria.

"Horsefeathers!" laughed the baroness. "I am just as selfish and petty as the next person. It's just that I am enjoying this so much. I can't do any of it myself. But I know something great when I see it. At least I have that much common sense."

Maria added several hours of writing to her daily schedule.

Far from being a chore, it was something she looked forward to at the end of each day. She sat in a wicker chair overlooking a green valley, writing a summary of her work. It included history, specifics about child development, and an entire explanation of Casa dei Bambini—all of the things she had been speaking about during the past month. The words came easily, and she finished by the time the course ended in late August. By graduation day, Maria's book, which came to be known as *The Montessori Method*, was ready for publication.

Graduation day for the first class of teachers dawned hot and sticky. By midafternoon, thunderclouds appeared over the hills of Città di Castello. It poured rain. The large terrace where they all sat faced the hills. They had been asked to dress in white, the color of renewal. At six o'clock, when the ceremony was to begin, a rainbow appeared. The crowd gasped.

"You are now Montessori teachers," Maria said. "You have studied here, passed written examinations, and done fifty hours of classroom observation. But more than that, you have rededicated your lives to service, to the common good of helping others, to allowing children to find their freedom and to fulfill their God-given potential. In doing so, you have been changed. This commitment is a prophecy of a brave and hopeful new world to come."

The graduates stood, received their certificates of completion one by one, and went indoors to a reception given by the Franchettis. Maria, the Annas, and Elizabeth Ballerini were joined by three of the American guests, Anne E. George, Dorothy Canfield Fisher, and Josephine Tozier. They all sat talking long into the evening.

"I'm hungry," Maria finally said. "We have talked so long. I propose we go into the kitchen, where I will make you pasta."

The amazed guests sat in the large estate kitchen while Maria cut tomatoes, sliced garlic, rolled out dough for pasta, and grated cheese. She insisted on doing everything herself. They watched as she gracefully moved about the room, doing her work with precision and care. There was joy in her focus. The same joy they heard when she spoke and saw when she worked with children. All who shared that midnight meal knew it was an evening they would cherish forever.

Anne E. George founded the first Montessori school in America in Tarrytown, New York. The students were all the children of wealthy sophisticates. The school was in a grand home overlooking the Hudson River north of New York City. It could not have been more different than the first Casa dei Bambini. Yet, as Maria had said, Anne E. George found that children are the same the world over.

Dorothy Canfield Fisher wrote several books about the Montessori Method. Josephine Tozier published a series of articles for *McClure's* magazine that made Maria Montessori a household name in America.

During the next three years, from 1910–1912, Maria continued to oversee the openings of new schools. She traveled, when she could, to see the first days at schools in Paris, Switzerland, and the Netherlands. She lectured for the University of Rome. Increasingly, her thoughts turned toward teacher training. She decided it was time to leave the University of Rome.

"You must follow your heart, Maria," Renilde Montessori counseled. "Ever since you were a tiny child, you have known you had a special mission in life. You have found it."

"I do have fears, I will admit," answered her daughter. "Now

I must support myself and you solely from my work in the Montessori world."

"God will provide," said Renilde. "He always does."

Maria spent the last months of 1912 holding two additional teacher training courses. She returned to Rome for the Christmas holidays. A cold sleet was falling, and she was glad to see her own front door. It was dinnertime. She anticipated the wonderful smell of her mother's cooking.

The lights were dim as she climbed the stairs. When she opened the door, she was met with a cold, gray silence. Then she heard her father's slow step down the hallway. His shoulders were bowed.

"Your mother," he said. "It happened an hour ago. The doctor is with her."

Maria dropped her bag. Alessandro put his hand on her shoulder, "Only palliative care now. That is what the doctor—" His voice broke. He looked toward the ceiling, as if in silent prayer. Maria saw the pain in his eyes.

She walked slowly down the hall and opened the door to her parents' bedroom. The family doctor sat by the bed.

"It was a massive stroke," he said. "She is resting comfortably. She may go in and out of consciousness, as you know."

"Thank you," said Maria. "I will stay with her. We will call you if we need you."

Maria sat by her mother's side for three days, holding her hand. There were a few brief moments when Renilde opened her eyes and looked deeply into her daughter's eyes. For forty-two years, Renilde had protected and championed Maria. Their bond had been unbroken. She had encouraged her and fed her body and soul. Now she was leaving the earth.

Early in the evening of December 20, 1912, Maria heard

carolers in the streets. "Sleep in heavenly peace," they sang. "Sleep in heavenly peace." Just before midnight, Renilde's eyes fluttered open. Maria saw in them the perfect love they had always held for her. Renilde Montessori took a slight, gentle last breath. The room was suddenly cold and empty.

Maria rose and went to comfort her father. She showed no outward signs of the powerful emotions she was feeling.

Just before Christmas, Maria went to visit Mario. He was now attending a boarding school outside Florence. Maria arrived as the school day was ending. Adolescent boys milled about, jostling and in constant motion. The holidays were almost upon them, and their excitement showed. It was a gray December day turning to evening, and all of the boys were wearing uniforms and caps. It was hard to tell one from another. A light December rain edged toward sleet. Maria was dressed in black, the color of mourning.

A lone figure walked toward her, then broke into a run. Mario seemed to have grown several inches. He met her with warmth and strength.

"I am so sorry," he said, holding her in his arms. "I have prayed for you every day during this sad time. I love you so. And I think that you are not my auntie, but my mother, and Renilde was my grandmother, and now she is gone. I have known this for a long time. I understand why you weren't able to raise me. I am young, but I understand. I want to be your son. I want to be with you and never apart. Mother!"

At the sound of that word, tears rolled down Maria's cheeks. They mingled with the rain that had become a downpour. Mother and son seemed not to notice. They stood outside the entrance to the school, embracing, impervious to the wind and the rain. They vowed never to be separated again.

Chapter Nine

THE SOUL OF AN ENTREPRENEUR

On December 6, 1913, Samuel Sidney McClure stood at the bow of the USS *Cincinnati*. He was impatient for the ship to complete its journey across the Atlantic from Naples to Brooklyn. The circling cormorants told him they were not far from the island of Manhattan.

As the former publisher of one of America's foremost magazines, *McClure's*, he had made the trip innumerable times. He stared out at the early December ocean. It was gray, like the back of a whale. The waves began to roll, and Samuel McClure understood why no one else was on the upper deck. The sky was dark and brooding, and he could barely make out the horizon line.

"This boat carries precious cargo," he thought with a smile.

Maria Montessori, the great Italian educator, whom McClure had been pursuing for four years, about whom one of his best writers, Josephine Tozier, had written fifteen articles, was on board. Appearing in *McClure's*, Josephine Tozier's articles had prompted more response and more sales than any other in the magazine's history. The United States of America was primed for Maria Montessori.

"And it is mostly due to me and my magazine," thought McClure. "I hope she appreciates that."

There had been letters, visits, talks, and meetings with Maria Montessori to convince her to come. This trip was the result of endless effort. Meanwhile, things had changed drastically since Josephine Tozier first contacted him about this Italian phenomenon. Samuel McClure had lost control of his magazine. Sales had dropped. The board had taken over and ousted him. He was in debt. But voyages always gave him hope.

He thought of his widowed mother, traveling in steerage on a similar voyage from Ireland to America with three young boys. She raised them in utter poverty on a subsistence farm in Indiana. He thought of his hardscrabble life at Knox College in Galesburg, Illinois. It took him seven years to graduate. He sold newspapers door to door to get through. But in the end, he learned what people want to know about. He spent days and weeks sitting in their kitchens and listening to their stories, hearing their troubles and their triumphs.

McClure was convinced this is what made his magazine a success. He merely published the articles and stories he thought those people wanted to read. And he was right, dammit. If only his own restlessness hadn't gotten in the way.

People called him grandiose and impractical. And yes, he'd been unfaithful to his dear Hattie. He was ashamed of it. His father-in-law, one of his professors at Knox, had begged his daughter not to marry him. McClure had waited seven years for her. And he still loved her. But his very public affairs had put her through hell and caused him, and his magazine, to lose favor with the public.

Everyone at the magazine warned him his behavior would lead to disaster. Some abandoned him in disgust. Others, like Willa Cather, stood by him. He'd been instrumental in introducing the public to Rudyard Kipling, Arthur Conan Doyle, Jack London, Willa Cather, Sarah Orne Jewett, and the list went on. McClure believed Ida Tarbell's articles on Standard Oil and Lincoln Steffens's on the horror of the meat-packing plants, published in his magazine, had changed America forever, awakening the soul of progressive idealism.

But all that was in the past. There were days when he wondered if he would feel this ignominy forever. Then he found Maria Montessori.

It was Josephine Tozier who first alerted him to the miracles wrought by the Italian educator. McClure was immediately interested. He met her before seeing her in action. She struck him as attractive, strong, and warm, but slightly distant and reserved. It was in the schools where she shone. Then he saw her lecture. He had never witnessed such a response from an audience. He knew he had struck gold. He just had to get the gold to come to America.

Montessori was a woman, yes. And McClure always found women alternately fascinating and unpredictable. Ida Tarbell, the progenitor of journalistic muckraking. Willa Cather, arguably the best writer in America. Two examples of women he revered. And his beloved Hattie, who had stood by him day and night, a constant source of support and wisdom. Women surrounded him. He thought he understood them. But this Montessori woman was inscrutable. She was not at all what he expected.

She was clearly a genius when it came to children and education. McClure believed fervently in her theories. He felt that together they could bring a much-needed revolution to the

American educational system. He'd approached her on many visits to Rome to propose building Montessori schools and teacher training institutes all across America. He had also proposed taking over publishing all of her books, as well as manufacturing all the apparatus used in Montessori schools.

Montessori had already made arrangements with an American named Carl Byoir to manufacture and sell her apparatus through his publishing company, the House of Childhood. Byoir was pleased with his profits. The first printing of *The Montessori Method* in English had sold 17,000 copies. McClure figured that was just a hint of the potential market for Montessori in America. With even sixty percent of the profits from all the possibilities, his financial worries would be over.

But Montessori was not as pliable or agreeable as McClure had hoped. It took several expensive trips to Rome to convince her to come to America. She seemed endlessly concerned about maintaining the purity of her work. It was often hard to see her. She was slow and methodical in a way that put McClure, who was used to making quick decisions and "jumping into the fire," as he put it, on edge.

On his final visit to Rome, McClure was nearly down to his last penny. He tried not to let his desperation show. Montessori was upset by the formation of the Montessori Education Association in Washington, DC, without her input. When McClure pointed out that the president's daughter, Margaret Wilson, and the Alexander Graham Bells were on the committee, Montessori wasn't impressed. She continued to focus on control.

She was suspicious of Byoir and the House of Childhood. She saw Dorothy Canfield Fisher's first book, *A Montessori Mother*, as misleading the public. McClure tried to reassure her about all of these things. And, in the end, she agreed to come.

McClure scheduled Montessori lectures in New York City, Boston, Philadelphia, and Chicago. Although he was nearly at the end of his financial resources, he suggested that he come to Naples and escort her personally to America.

McClure was forced to engage an agent, Lee Keedick, to front the money to rent the halls and promote the lectures. Keedick would take a part of the profit for his investment. Tickets were selling far beyond expectations, and many venues were already sold out. McClure had not told Maria anything about Keedick. But he assumed that when she saw the crowds and the ticket sales, she wouldn't mind.

McClure had staked his future, his finances, and his professional life on Maria Montessori. Everything hinged on her.

Looking down to the second deck, he saw a lone figure dressed in black. The prow of the ship rose and fell as it turned slowly toward Manhattan. The figure moved slowly toward the ship's rail. A smaller figure followed, draped a plaid deck blanket around the first figure's shoulders, then retreated, battered by the wind. McClure could see that the figure in black was Maria Montessori.

Maria looked out to the horizon. It was six o'clock in the morning, and she had already eaten and dressed. Her heavy black skirt was whipped by the wind, and she grasped the blanket that Anna Fedeli had brought.

She found the fresh air and solitude bracing. The spray from the gigantic waves was a sort of baptism. She was eager to see America and to experience the culture and its people. She was anxious to reconnect with the many students and colleagues she had come to know. Most of all, she wanted to visit the Montessori schools in America.

Dark clouds scudded across the sky. Maria couldn't look at the sky without thinking of her mother. She kept a card with Renilde's photo in her pocket. It gave her comfort to look at it. Earlier in the year, she held a teacher training in their apartment in Rome. She knew Renilde would have loved the energy and optimism of the students.

Maria turned more and more often to Mario, who now lived with her, as a confidant. He never failed her. He encouraged her to go to America, but to be wary. Mario based his advice on stories he had heard about the American character.

"Americans are indeed a breed apart," thought Maria. "Samuel McClure must be an extreme example." She found their constant movement and endless aggressiveness disconcerting. She thought many American students showed great enthusiasm for her work but never went beyond the surface aspects. Without understanding the underlying principles, they focused solely on early reading, for example, or the misguided perception that children in Montessori schools were allowed to do whatever they liked.

Maria was appalled by Dorothy Canfield Fisher's book *A Montessori Mother* and its implication that one could pick and choose parts of her work and combine them with others. "The Montessori method is not a buffet," Maria thought. She was disturbed that the Montessori Education Association had been founded without her knowledge or approval.

Americans seemed to love to create organizations and do everything by committee. "I have poured nearly thirty years of my life into this," Maria vowed. "I do not function via committee, and I will not be dictated to by any committee or organization, American or not. I will simply make this clear."

Maria was also concerned about financial arrangements. She

was a woman alone, with a son and a father to support, along with an increasing number of employees. She had signed a contract with a man named Carl Byoir from the state of Iowa to manufacture and sell her apparatus in America. She had signed a contract to let McClure use a film about a Montessori school in Rome. The film was incredibly effective, during lectures, in providing visual proof of what Maria presented verbally.

Maria completely trusted the Baroness and Baron Franchetti, as profit was not their motive. She wasn't so sure about McClure. Maria recalled her father's advice to pick her battles. She would be strong, as she had always been. She would put the interests of the children first. She felt she was doing this by going to America. But no one was going to wrest control from her. And no one was going to profit unfairly from her work. She would see to that.

She took Renilde's picture from her pocket and held it up.

"I had a dream last night, dear mother," she said. "I dreamed I was rowing to America. Was this a good or a bad omen?" Suddenly a stiff wind blew over the prow and snatched the card out of Maria's hand. She watched it float down to the waves and disappear. "It seems I will need to be strong on my own in America," Maria thought.

She noticed many people gathering on the deck below. Despite the cold and the wind, they wanted to see the Statue of Liberty when it came into view.

Maria stood quietly on the deck. She saw the torch first. Then the statue, framed by gray clouds. A woman was welcoming her to America.

Maria went inside as the ship rounded Staten Island and Governor's Island before making its way to the dock in Brooklyn. She wanted to prepare herself for America.

~

The USS *Cincinnati* bumped and swayed as it came into the dock. Cabin boys rushed about, tilting trunks onto carts. McClure appeared, dressed in a bowler hat and overcoat. He offered his arm to Maria as they descended the gangplank.

Maria was amazed to see huge banners attached to the dock that read "Welcome Maria Montessori." A band was playing a rollicking tune. Reporters scrambled up the gangplank and bulbs began flashing.

Anne E. George was a welcome sight. She waved to Maria and said "Welcome to America!" in Italian. She had learned to speak Italian so she could be Maria's translator in America.

"What is the song they are playing?" yelled Maria over the din.

"It's called 'Snooky Ookums,'" Anne yelled back. "It's a song by Irving Berlin."

"Snooky what? Irving where?" asked Maria, smiling in spite of herself.

A crowd of reporters nearly knocked them over. A man stepped quickly out of the crowd. "Hey, fellas, it's freezing out here! I told, you, press conference at the Holland House. Now skedaddle and let the lady catch a breath."

He had a large chin and wore a wool coat in kelly green. He took Maria's hand and kissed it. "Lee Keedick here, agent, manager, and handler of these ruffians. I'll be with you all the way."

Maria turned to Anne for clarification.

"He says he is an agent, and he is going to be handling you."

"And who is paying him for this?" Maria thought. But she said nothing. Her face remained impassive. But she would let them all know that she was more than capable of handling herself.

She stepped away from Keedick and McClure and took Anne's elbow. She walked into the center of the scrum of reporters. Her calm, confident demeanor gave them all pause. She seemed not to notice the light rain, which was slowly turning to sleet, or the stiff wind, which blew out her skirts and her wool cape.

"I'll be damned if she doesn't look like 'Winged Victory,'" Keedick said to McClure.

"I am honored that you have all come to meet me," said Maria, "I will answer all of your questions. I invite you all to the Holland House, where I am staying, so that we can discuss children, the future of our world, and a peaceful world. Hopefully there will be a fireplace so that you can warm yourselves. But first, I have three questions for you.

"Where is your Lower East Side from here? I have heard it is the area in your city most like the San Lorenzo, where I started Casa dei Bambini. Secondly, are Americans always in a hurry? And third, I have heard of your egg cream. And I would like one."

The reporters scribbled furiously as Anne E. George translated. They laughed and shouted answers in response to Maria's questions.

Keedick and McClure exchanged relieved glances. Maria Montessori obviously knew how to manage the press. She didn't need their help. Whatever discomfort or shyness she might display one-on-one disappeared in front of a crowd.

"And now I look forward to crossing your famous Brooklyn Bridge to the fabled island of Manhattan," Maria announced in closing. She walked slowly toward a waiting car, the calm center in a swirling vortex.

Soon Maria, Anne, McClure, and Keedick were on their way. The rain had turned to sleet that pelted the car windows. It was ten o'clock in the morning but looked like dusk. As the car turned north from lower Manhattan, McClure pointed out City Hall and the recently completed Woolworth Building, the pride of New York City. Maria and Anne craned their necks to see the top of the skyscraper.

"It is like a cathedral, but a cathedral of commerce," Keedick said.

Anne translated, and Maria leaned her head against the back of the leather seat, contemplating this image and what it implied. Her attention was quickly taken by an altercation on the sidewalk at Twenty-Third and Fifth. A car had overrun the curb and smashed a pushcart. An angry crowd had gathered, and Maria could discern Spanish, Italian, and Yiddish among the shouting. The driver of their car screamed at the pedestrians to get out of the way. Moments later, they arrived at Thirtieth and Fifth Avenue, the entrance to Holland House.

"Was that typical for New York City?" Maria asked.

"Was what typical?" McClure responded.

"The huge crowd. The raised voices. The cacophony of languages."

"I didn't even notice it," said McClure.

"Why is this place called Holland House?" Maria wanted to know. She was endlessly curious. "I am enamored of the Netherlands. There are already some Montessori schools there. Is Holland House a Dutch hotel?"

This time, Keedick answered. "It probably just sounded good. You know, a marketing trick."

As their car stopped, reporters surged down the steps of the entrance. Maria exited the car, walked up the marble steps and entered the lobby. A large chair was waiting near a roaring fireplace. She sat.

"You don't want to rest first?" said an astonished Samuel McClure.

"I don't need to. I promised to answer questions. I will be here until each journalist is satisfied," Maria said.

"Little lady, that might take all day," Keedick said with a guffaw.

Maria smiled beatifically. "I am not little, but I am a lady. And ladies keep their promises."

True to her word, Maria sat for hours answering questions that ranged from education theory to her thoughts on motherhood and the suffragette movement.

"Are you a feminist?" one reporter asked.

"I believe that what broadens the mother broadens the child," Maria said.

The reporter wrote that down, then pondered it.

McClure stood anxiously at the back of the room. Good press was the key to his success. His own magazine had sparked and accelerated interest in Maria Montessori among thousands of Americans. But the daily newspapers would provide the first impressions of the Italian educator. The journalists in the lobby were the eyes and ears of the American public.

Maria spoke with reporters and fans, greeted students and signed copies of her book. She did it all with patience, forbearance, and a slight detachment. She arrived in her room at the Holland House nearly six hours after disembarking in Brooklyn.

She had an entire suite at the Holland House to herself. It was filled with brocade sofas, lace bedcovers, and vases filled with roses. "Who is paying for all of this extravagance?" she wondered. She looked out a window at the street below.

Fifth Avenue was teeming with life. A group of suffragettes handed out pamphlets. A richly dressed mother pulled a little boy away from a window filled with a Christmas display. A servant followed behind, laden with shiny shopping bags. A bedraggled child sat with his back against the building, near a heating grate, offering pencils for sale. No one was buying. He looked for all the world like Antonio, one of the first children at Casa dei Bambini. It was for children like him that she had come to America.

Maria's debut lecture in America would take place in Washington, DC. A tour to Chicago, Philadelphia, and Boston would follow, and a final lecture at Carnegie Hall in New York City. Everything was completely sold out.

Samuel McClure visited Maria in her suite in Washington, DC, on the morning of the first lecture. "I wanted to go over how the evening will work," he said.

Maria said nothing.

McClure plunged on. "I thought I would speak about McClure's magazine, the history of your work, how crowds and educators have responded to you. Then show the films that are really, as we say here, the proof in the pudding. Then you can say a few words to finish things out."

Maria replied in measured tones, "I have successfully lectured in Europe for over fifteen years. This is how it will go. There will be a short, possibly five-minute introduction. Then I will come onto the stage. I will speak about Casa dei Bambini and how I arrived at my theories: the science and anthropology that is the foundation of what I do and what I believe. I will speak about the rights of women and children and the freedom of the soul to create the kind of society in which we all want to live, with peace and justice for all.

"This is what people will come to hear, and this is the whole reason for my trip to America. And yes, I am very familiar with your expression about the pudding. I have the proof in the pudding for many years now, as evidenced by the proliferation of Montessori schools throughout Europe and America."

There was an uneasy silence. Then McClure cleared his throat and said, "American audiences are different than European audiences. I was just thinking about making things move along."

"I am not interested in making things move along," said Maria. "I am interested in the human soul. I believe all human beings want the same thing. To be treated with dignity and respect and to aspire to their highest potential."

She stood abruptly. "And now I must prepare for this evening. I bid you a good day. A day in which you will, I hope, achieve your potential. I will see you at the lecture hall. And if someone can bring me an egg cream, that would be lovely. I had one yesterday, and I believe it brought me good luck." She guided McClure to the door and shut it behind him.

Maria's arrival at Union Station in Washington, DC, was as crowded and triumphal as her entry into New York City. Margaret Wilson, the president's daughter, and the Alexander Graham Bells held a reception in her honor.

Maria understood they were behind the formation of the Montessori Education Association. She believed in their fervor. But she was increasingly alarmed by the American attitude of adapting the Montessori system to American culture. To Maria, this displayed a total lack of understanding. The basis of her work was to provide the child with a series of stimuli perfectly adapted to his or her exact developmental stage.

Maria stopped counting the number of well-dressed, well-meaning women who came up to her saying, "I bought your entire kit, your whole apparatus from the House of Childhood. We have it in our home and our children play with it." She asked one woman how much the kit had cost. When the woman replied "Fifty dollars," Maria was stunned. She knew it cost twelve dollars to manufacture. Someone was making a huge profit. Maria had not seen a penny.

Maria's lecture in Washington, DC, was attended by members of Congress, senators and their wives, and by celebrities and dignitaries such as Alexander Graham Bell and Margaret Wilson. President Woodrow Wilson was scheduled to attend but cancelled due to ill health.

If there were skeptics in the audience, they seemed, at the lecture's end, to be thoroughly convinced that the self-determination, self-motivation, and self-discipline outlined by the Montessori method were not only compatible but necessary for American children. Maria received a standing ovation and was surrounded by crowds asking questions and begging for her presence in their city or institution.

Maria Montessori in America had made a grand beginning. McClure and Keedick were thrilled.

Anne E. George was able to spirit Maria to her suite aboard the train bound for Philadelphia the next day for an afternoon rest. She marveled at Maria's stamina. Maria had given two lectures in Washington, attended three receptions and talked at length with endless lines of people.

She was surrounded constantly by admirers whenever she

was in public. As her translator, Anne had to maintain Maria's exact schedule. Anne was exhausted, deep in her bones. Maria was closing her eyes when a knock came on the door.

It was a porter with three huge satchels of mail. "These arrived for Dr. Montessori." The porter roughly slammed the satchels on the floor of the moving train. One split open and a cascade of mail slid out.

Maria and Anne began to sort through it. There were many bills. Maria was now her father's caretaker. There were bills from schools, requests for lectures, for teacher training, from educators all over the world. The two women sat in the midst of it all.

"It has snowed mail," said Maria with a laugh.

"You go through all of this yourself?" Anne asked, astounded. "You are responsible for all of this?"

"My mother used to help me. Anna Fedeli, Anna Maccheroni, and a few others in Rome are all angels at my side." Anne E. George began to grasp the weight of Maria's responsibilities. She gazed in admiration at Maria, who rested her head against the sofa seat and promptly fell asleep.

The next day, December 8, was one Maria had been anticipating for months. Helen Keller, the activist and author, and Annie Sullivan, her teacher, were coming to visit. When they arrived, the four women—Maria, Keller, Sullivan, and Anne E. George—stood together in a silent embrace for several minutes.

Keller spoke through Sullivan and was translated carefully by Anne E. George. "We have both overcome so many obstacles, and there are many more to come," Keller said. "But our mutual goal of liberty and freedom for the soul will give us strength."

In Chicago, the next stop on the tour, Maria met the activist and reformer Jane Addams and visited Hull House, founded by Addams, to welcome and assist immigrants in all aspects of their lives.

Maria was deeply moved by these meetings.

She traveled on to Boston, where she lectured for the faculty at Harvard University, then back to New York City for her final two lectures at Carnegie Hall. There was a near riot outside Carnegie Hall on the night of Maria's first lecture. Almost one thousand people had been denied tickets. The hall was filled to capacity.

Samuel McClure gave Maria Montessori a brief introduction. She walked onstage to thunderous applause. She took in the entire audience, and even in the depths of the cavernous hall, her luminous eyes and warm presence created an intimacy that mesmerized the crowd.

She spoke of the history behind her work, her study of Itard and Seguin, the scientific foundation of her background, and the creation of Casa dei Bambini. She emphasized the importance of education as a means to a peaceful, unified world. The program ended with a film of the children in their classroom at Casa de Bambini.

The ovation at the end seemed to last forever. The audience wouldn't let her leave the stage. As Maria bowed, taking in their appreciation, she saw McClure and Keedick in the wings. They were holding a large ledger book. They looked very pleased. Maria realized they were counting receipts. "And I have not seen a penny," she thought.

Meanwhile, a woman had climbed the steps at the side of the stage to stand before her. "I've come all the way from Yonkers, and I want to know how I can get my little Jimmy to behave," she said.

Maria stood for another hour, speaking with well-wishers and answering all manner of questions. Anne finally brought her backstage. Keedick and McClure were still bent over the ledger. They closed it when they saw Maria.

"This is the last thing you need to worry over," said Keedick with a smile.

"Correction," said Maria. "After the children, who are my first reason for this tour, I'd say it is the second most important thing. Spirituality without practicality is an imbalance. You forget I am a scientist. I never worry. But I do observe. The root of the word suspicion is to observe. Did you know that? I see everything. Good evening, gentleman."

Maria boarded the *Lusitania* on the morning of Christmas Eve 1913. She felt her American tour had been a triumph. She pushed away thoughts about the motives of McClure and Keedick. She began writing a letter to the Montessori Education Association, outlining the parameters of how any further work would proceed. First, she and she alone would be in charge of all teacher training. No teacher who wasn't personally trained by Maria Montessori would be a Montessori teacher or qualified to open a Montessori school. This seemed to be the only way to assure perspective, understanding, and conformity to the principles she had worked thirty years to develop.

Maria arrived in Rome in a state of complete exhaustion. The moment she saw Mario standing at the train station, her spirits lifted. She hadn't realized how wary she had been, how full of questions and concerns, especially regarding Samuel McClure. It was a relief to be back with someone she trusted so completely.

"I have a present for you, Mother," said Mario, handing her

a small box tied with a ribbon. It was a tiny butterfly pin made of papier-mâché. "I made it for you," he said with a smile. "I also have some other things to discuss with you. I have been doing research, while you were gone, on Mr. McClure. I found some old issues of the New York Times and had them translated. Did you know he lost his business, McClure's magazine, and was nearly bankrupt? Your sense that he was interested in profiting from your work was not altogether wrong."

"There is nothing wrong with earning a fair wage for fair work," Maria said.

"No, not at all," Mario agreed.

"But he didn't tell me anything about his situation. That disturbs me. I now see that he had to bring Lee Keedick along to provide money. I felt this all along, a sense of desperation. And now I understand it."

Letters from McClure began to arrive. Soon after the New Year, Maria received a check from the House of Childhood for five hundred dollars. Maria estimated that Carl Byoir had made a minimum of $60,000 from the sale of her apparatus. She also received a check from Lee Keedick. All of the expenses for the trip, including Keedick's and McClure's, had been deducted from her share of the profits.

Maria's blood ran cold.

Alessandro Montessori was resting. He was a man in his eighties now, and he often rested during the day. Mario was bent over a book.

"I am going for a walk, my dear," Maria said to Mario. "I need to reacquaint myself with Rome."

She was shaking with anger and didn't want her son to see. She had been lied to and manipulated. She had been used. Further, the Americans seemed intent on changing, adapting, and abusing her ideas in order to profit from them. She walked and walked, ignoring the sights around her, deciding what to do next.

Maria found herself in front of the Basilica of Our Lady in Trastevere. She went inside. The smooth marble floor, the smell of incense, and the dome painted with the Ascension gave her comfort. She stopped shaking. She knelt down to pray. She thought of her mother, and of Helen Keller, who had told her, "Although the world is full of suffering, it is also full of the overcoming of it."

Maria left the church. The early January twilight was just descending. Street lamps were beginning to light up.

"I will never again allow anyone to misuse me or the Montessori name," Maria vowed. "I will remain vigilant in protecting the work, the training of the teachers, and most of all, the children of the world. I will trust my son and the handful of the faithful who have been with me from the beginning. Neither Samuel McClure nor anyone ever again will use what I have created for their own gain. I will set all policies from this moment on."

She heard someone say, "Mother." She turned to see Mario walking toward her.

"I came to find you," he said. "You were gone so long I knew you were upset. I knew I would find you here, in this sacred place."

"I love this place, and I love you," Maria said. Together they walked arm-in-arm across the piazza in front of the basilica. They sat on the edge of the fountain in the center, talking and laughing, while the lights along the street came on one by one. Then they went home to dinner.

≈

Robert McClure, Samuel McClure's brother, got lost several times on the winding cobbled streets of Rome. It was May 1914. He was there because his brother had talked him into it. He didn't want to come. But Samuel felt it was way past time to solidify a contractual agreement with Maria Montessori.

McClure had appealed to Robert's ego, saying that his brother's charm and good looks would surely appeal to Maria Montessori. Besides, McClure was too busy to make the crossing himself. He was preparing to open Montessori schools in America. He needed that agreement. The future of the McClure family and their fortunes hinged on Robert getting Maria Montessori to sign. This would allow the McClure publicity machine to go into high gear, promoting Montessori schools and teacher training institutes all over the country. The money would roll in.

Robert was tired, nervous, and confused by the voices chattering around him in a language he didn't understand. The cobblestones hurt his feet, and he wondered why all the streets had such long names. "Haven't they ever heard of Main Street? Or how about Broadway?" he thought.

He finally found Via Principessa Clotilde and the Montessori apartment. He took a deep breath and lifted the heavy knocker. It echoed loudly, and in a few moments Maria herself appeared at the door. Her direct gaze was unnerving. She offered him the slightest smile.

"Please come in, Mr. McClure," she said. They walked up a stone stairway. "Haven't these people heard of elevators?" he thought.

They arrived in her office. It was full of framed photographs of students and, he presumed, family members. A darkly handsome young man stood in the corner and gave a bow. "I am

Mario, and I have been studying English. I will be translating."
The young gentleman had the same gaze as Maria Montessori.

Robert began to curse his brother silently. Maria walked around her desk, sat in her chair, and looked at him. She didn't invite Robert to sit. There was a long pause. Clearly it was up to him to begin.

"Have you seen silent films?" he asked. "Hal Roach, a famous director, has a favorite saying. 'Cut to the chase.' It means get to the point."

"I am very familiar with silent films," said Maria. "In fact, a film was made of my work with children in Rome. Your brother has it, even though he is not authorized to have it. I would like it back. That is just one of the things we will address."

Robert cleared his throat and tried a different tack. "Promoted successfully by McClure's magazine, your trip to America continues to be regarded as a great triumph."

"Without my thirty years of study, work, observation, and the creation of a new theory of education for children, McClure's magazine would have had nothing to promote," said Maria.

Robert was becoming flustered. "The Montessori Education Association, headed by none other than President Wilson's daughter, is doing a great job of keeping Montessori schools alive and promoting their growth in America."

"I was never consulted about the formation of the association, nor have I been asked to participate. I find this outrageous. Furthermore. the percentage of profit that I have made from Carl Byoir's sale of my apparatus is ludicrous. But my lawyer is handling that."

"How sad that we are beginning our talk with words like percentages and sales," Robert said in his most mollifying tone.

"I know you are a spiritual woman, Maria. Aren't the children the point of all this? Their trusting eyes, their trusting hearts, and the nurturing of their souls?"

Maria stood up and walked around her desk to face Robert McClure directly.

"How dare you mention the word trust? Or refer to children. Your brother has lied and misled me from the very beginning. He was nearly penniless and had lost the magazine. He wanted to exploit me for profit. If he had been honest from the beginning about his situation, we could have had common ground.

"You seem to think that because I am a woman and I am spiritual I don't understand precisely what you are doing or have tried to do. I am a woman who gave up a medical practice to devote her life to this work. I have a family to support. But I have never for one moment had any other motive than the education and betterment of children and their families.

"I don't expect someone whose only motive is profit to understand. I have written a letter to your Montessori Education Association and to the London Times Educational Supplement, which all educators read. It states that I wish to control all of my work. No teacher who is not personally trained by me can call herself or himself a Montessori teacher or open a Montessori school. No one—not you, not your brother or anyone else—will ever exploit me or my work again.

"I have nothing more to say to you or to your brother, who is a coward for not coming here himself. I will never sign any kind of contract that promotes any further relationship, business or otherwise, between myself and your brother. And now, Mario, would you be so kind as to escort Mr. McClure out?"

Mario led Robert McClure down the stairs that led to the street. Robert was white as a sheet.

"Is there anything I can do for you, Mr. McClure?" he asked.

"Yes. You can point me toward the train station, if I can find it through these damn winding streets, and get me the hell out of this country."

As he started walking away, Mario called after him. "Sir, you are walking the wrong way!" Robert McClure waved him off.

Mario returned to his mother's office. She greeted him with a wide smile. "We have been invited to San Francisco in America, to the Panama-Pacific International Exposition!" she exclaimed, handing him a letter.

Mario was incredulous. "Haven't you had enough of America?"

"I've had enough of certain Americans. But it is a large country. This time, we are going to the western side of America, to California. And there is another thing that makes all the difference," she said.

"Yes?" asked Mario.

"I will be with you."

Chapter Ten

THE SOUL OF A LEADER

On June 28, 1914, Archduke Franz Ferdinand of Austria was assassinated in Sarajevo and the first World War began. It spread quickly throughout Europe. Despite the dangers of travel, Maria and Anna Maccheroni decided to open a Montessori school in Barcelona in 1915. Spain had remained neutral, and over several trips, Maria had seen how much support there was for her work in that city. Maria and Mario would go to America, and Anna would open the school.

Anna arrived in Barcelona in May 1915. She had taken a night train from Rome. When the official came to check her passport at the border, her hand shook so badly the official leaned down and said, "Don't worry, Spaniards don't bite." He laughed, smoothed his bristly mustache, and clicked away, whistling under his breath.

Anna had not slept a wink. She had never been to another country.

"You must believe, Anna, that you have the strength to do

this, the power to accomplish great things," Maria had told her before leaving for the exposition. "God is on your side. If you remember this is for the children and not about ourselves, it will keep things in perspective."

Anna knew that Maria was saying two things: that she believed in her, and the only possible answer was yes. By now, Maria Montessori was traveling all over Europe.

Anna stepped from the train into a brilliant, sunny Barcelona day. "I am doing this for the future of children," she told herself. "And for Maria, who has given me confidence."

The sky was azure blue. A young woman wearing a white dress, blue sash, and red scarf came to greet her. "My name is Alicia," she said. Her brown eyes were welcoming. She spoke Italian. She explained that Barcelona was part of the Catalan culture. "The Catalans want to bring Montessori to all of Spain, but here we begin. Beginnings are good, yes?"

Anna was charmed. Her shoulders began to relax. She felt she could breathe for the first time in days. She tried to remember what Maria had told her. She gazed out the window and saw a series of strangely sloping buildings. The roofs seemed to undulate, and Anna wondered aloud if she was dizzy.

"You are perfectly well," Alicia laughed. "This is the work of the Catalan genius architect, Antonio Gaudi. He is bringing Catalan architecture to modernism. Soon this will be a park with beautiful buildings and places for all who live in Barcelona to feel more human and to be in nature. This is why we have brought you here. This is the message of Maria Montessori, too, no? She is a genius, yes?"

The taxi stopped in front of a series of low white stucco buildings. The window sashes were painted bright blue. White lace curtains fluttered in the breeze. The window boxes held pots of red geraniums. The effect was welcoming and cheerful.

"The children are waiting inside to meet you," Alicia said.

Anna Maccheroni stepped inside the schoolroom. She saw typical desks and benches and made a mental note about changing them. There were five children, all dressed in snow-white uniforms. They ranged in age from three to seven. They held hands and stood stiffly against the back wall of the room. They looked like tiny ghosts.

They politely greeted Anna by bowing their heads, but otherwise they didn't move. Except for the noise from the street, the room was completely silent. Anna thought of the talkative, rowdy children at the Casa dei Bambini in Rome and Milan. The contrast was daunting.

As the days in Barcelona began to unfold, the children, who were unused to having any stimulation whatsoever, had to be encouraged. Anna was careful not to direct or prod them. Slowly and gradually, the Catalan children began to use the materials. Anna placed them on low shelves she had built on one side of the room. She lay small rugs, purchased at a nearby market, on the floor, and had the desks and benches removed. She convinced the administrators to let the children dress themselves, wash themselves, serve and clean up after themselves. The Catalans were amazed that children could do these things. Word got out and the school grew quickly. Within six months, there would be one hundred children.

Anna began to explore Barcelona. She was astounded by the Sagrada Familia, the cathedral Gaudi was building, and decided to share it with her students, who had never been on a field trip. She took them to see Gaudi himself at work on the cathedral.

Pointing out his painstaking work on the mosaics, she said, "One step at a time, children. That is how you build a cathedral. It is how you learn. It is how you build a life." Anna grew to love the city and wrote to Maria about it nearly every day.

She lived simply in a room not far from her school. One Saturday morning, she walked to the seashore. She saw red boats bobbing in the water. Sailors were pulling in a catch of fish. Sailboats were silently gliding in the harbor. Anna sat in the sand. It had been warmed by the sun. She desired nothing more, wanted nothing more than this glorious moment.

She thought back to nine years ago, when she had wondered if her life was worth living. She had found her purpose in life through the work of Maria Montessori. She vowed she would spend the rest of her life sharing it with others. She knew there were many people who had found similar purpose through Maria and her mission.

After a morning spent looking out to sea, Anna walked slowly up the hill to write a long letter to Maria. She wanted to tell her all about each student and the glory of Barcelona. She dared to think that perhaps Spain would be a good place to live permanently and to establish a nationwide Montessori school system.

Maria and Mario began their American stay in Los Angeles. The sweet fragrance of orange blossoms enveloped them as they stepped down from the train at Union Station. Helen Parkhurst was there to greet them. Born in Wisconsin, she had taught in one-room schools and had completed Maria's teacher training course in Rome. She was young, dynamic, and eager to be Maria's assistant on her second trip to the States.

She came bearing gifts: two large straw hats she had purchased on Olivera Street, the site of the founding of Los Angeles. "It is very sunny here, and you will need these to protect your beautiful skin," she said. "All the movie stars wear them."

Helen Parkhurst had found a small Spanish adobe home to rent on Virgil Street in a hilly section of Los Angeles called Los Feliz. Maria could look out to see orange trees and red-tiled roofs dotting the hillsides.

The days were warm and sunny. Maria made breakfasts of fresh orange juice and marmalade toast each morning. Maria, Mario, and Helen sat on the patio attached to the kitchen. It opened onto a small garden, and four curious neighborhood children liked to visit. Maria soon began to interact with them using some of the materials she had brought with her.

Their schedule was packed, with lectures and training courses in San Diego and Los Angeles. Mail routed from Rome and Barcelona piled up. Exhausted by her schedule and the pressures of daily interviews and lectures, Maria could often be found in the garden, her head in her hands, sitting among stacks of letters. Mario would put his arms around her and comfort her. Helen Parkhurst was touched when she found them this way. She understood that Mario was Maria's son, but it was never mentioned.

A young woman named Helen Christy was part of the teacher training in Los Angeles. She had a serious demeanor and large blue eyes. She offered to help Maria and Mario. Helen Christy proved to be immensely organized, and Maria came to rely on her gratefully. Arriving home late one day to the house on Virgil Street, Maria smelled something delicious cooking. She heard laughing voices and walked into the kitchen. She saw Mario snapping a dish towel at Helen Christy as she giggled and said, "You are not helping at all, Mario. There is garlic to slice and a table to set. I am supposed to be helping, not playing."

"What if I don't want to? Are you going to make me?"

"You silly—"

They both saw Maria at the same time. All she said was, "Whatever that is smells wonderful."

Soon it was time to leave Los Angeles for San Francisco and the Panama-Pacific International Exposition. A special Montessori school in the Hall of Education was almost ready to open. Early one evening, Maria and Helen Christy were sitting in the garden, sorting through piles of mail, when she heard a knock on the door. Helen Christy rose to answer it.

She returned with a tiny young woman whose golden hair hung in ringlets down her back. She wore a black cloche hat and a white shawl. She walked onto the patio saying, "Oh, it is so lovely here! I am Mary Pickford. I apologize for bothering you at home. But I came to honor you, to tell you how interested I am in everything you have to say and everything you stand for. I want to help start a Montessori school here in Hollywood."

Mario and Helen Christy were starstruck. They had just seen Mary Pickford in "Tess of the Storm Country." She was arguably the most famous woman in the world. And here she was, sitting on an old wicker chair on their patio.

"You must stay with us for dinner, Miss Pickford," said Maria. There was a pause while Mary Pickford's large eyes looked from Helen Christy to Maria to Mario, as if asking whether they really wanted her to stay.

"Why, yes," she said with a glorious smile. "That would be delightful."

They sat together, the twenty-three-year-old actress,

the forty-five-year-old educator, and the two young people, balancing their plates on their knees. Mary shared stories of early poverty and struggle, of demanding her fair share of salary and recognition from Adolph Zukor, the producer. Maria shared stories of resilience in the face of fierce opposition to her desire to become a doctor. She made potato gnocchi, and they ate with relish as the sun faded and the evening breeze rustled the trees. Helen Christy brought a quilt to put around Mary's thin shoulders. Mary seemed not to want to leave.

"I am called to the set at six o'clock in the morning, and it comes early. So I suppose I must go," Mary finally said. Maria walked Mary to the large black car that was waiting for her. A burly driver flicked a cigarette butt out the door when he saw them coming.

"Those two young people, Mario and Helen, are in love," Mary said with a silvery laugh. "But you know that. I remember that feeling." Her voice turned wistful.

"Yes," said Maria. "I have felt like that, too. There is nothing like it."

"It is a mystery of life that something so beautiful can bring such pain," Mary said. "I hope they stay in the beauty part for a long time. I know you'll bless them." Mary reached up impulsively and hugged Maria tightly. Then she was off.

The next day, Mario and Helen Christy came to Maria. They told her they wanted to marry and start a Montessori school in Hollywood. Maria's heart sank. She couldn't imagine going on to San Francisco without Mario. She needed him.

"I will always be with you in spirit, Mother," he said. "I will always come to you if you need me."

Maria thought of Mary Pickford's words. Then she said, "I

bless you, son, and your whole life. Stay here with Helen. I know you love her. Take care of her, and of your love. Helen Parkhurst will go with me to the exposition."

"It is like an entire city!" Helen Parkhurst exclaimed as they entered the Panama-Pacific Exposition grounds. "It is almost as if they put Rome inside San Francisco." They strolled through huge stone archways that opened onto plazas. Fountains with statues in their centers rose up from ponds filled with lilies. Trees and lush gardens everywhere invited visitors to enjoy the world created by the Pan-Pacific planners.

In one courtyard, they came upon a statue of a pioneer woman, a lifelike tribute to the American spirit. She gazed up to the sky and stood with her arms outstretched, as if reaching toward the future with confidence. Maria and Helen loved this statue and visited it often during their time at the exposition.

A huge spire pointed to the sky, dwarfing all other sites. It was the Tower of Jewels, 450 feet high, covered with 100,000 pieces of colored glass that reflected the sun and moved with the wind.

The first World War was raging in Europe, and America was torn between involvement and isolationism. The dark crisis in Europe dominated the headlines. Perhaps that strengthened the zeal to celebrate the ingenuity and creativity of humankind. Billed as a celebration of the opening of the Panama Canal, the exposition was also a rebirth for the city of San Francisco after the devastating earthquake of 1906. City officials spared no expense and built the exposition on 623 acres of land overlooking San Francisco Bay. It was a world apart from the sinking of the *Lusitania* and the other horrors of war. Despite the conflict, nearly every country participated in the exposition.

Clutching maps, Helen Parkhurst and Maria Montessori walked through the massive Palace of Fine Arts, with its oval plaza opening onto the Palace of Education and Social Economy.

On the train to San Francisco, they pored over nearly two thousand applications to their laboratory school, which would be in a glass enclosure within the Palace of Education. Maria stipulated that she wanted only children with no prior schooling. She insisted on a variety of cultures and social backgrounds. Parents wrote letters begging for their children to be accepted. Helen and Maria had chosen thirty students. Their parents had all been notified. Among them were General John J. Pershing's two daughters.

Entering the Palace of Education, Maria and Helen headed for the glass enclosure. For the next four months, it would be a public classroom for thirty children five days a week, from nine o'clock until noon. It would be known as the Montessori Glass Classroom.

Rows of bleachers surrounded it on all sides. There would be no escaping the constant gaze of the curious public. Inside, small pieces of furniture designed to Maria's specifications stood ready. Shelves were lined with her apparatus, dishes, sinks, towels, brooms, and dustpans, all set to receive students. Everything was ready.

Maria and Helen made their way to the Fairmont Hotel on Nob Hill, where they were besieged by dignitaries and well-wishers. In a quiet moment, Maria turned to Helen. "Tomorrow, our first day at the exposition, I am scheduled to address thousands of educators at a convention here in San Francisco."

"How can you do that and be at the laboratory school?" Helen asked.

"I know a great deal about science, but I have never learned how to be in two places at once. You have become like a daughter to me. I have confidence in you."

"About what?" asked Helen, with a dawning realization.

"I believe that you can begin our work at the laboratory school while I speak to the convention. I'm afraid it is the only way. You and Mario are the only ones I trust. And Mario is hobnobbing with Helen Christy and Mary Pickford in Hollywood."

Maria saw the look on Helen Parkhurst's face. "Don't be afraid. I have never been so sure of anything."

Helen Parkhurst arrived at the exposition at six o'clock the next morning, as street sweepers were making the boulevards ready for the day's crowds. An early morning fog hung in the air. She went straight to the French Pavilion for breakfast. Shortly before eight o'clock, she was at the Glass Classroom, waiting for the first family to arrive. It was General Pershing with his daughters.

By nine o'clock, all of the children had taken their places inside the enclosure. Helen began to demonstrate handwashing at the small wash basins. She gave each child a white apron. She showed them the materials and how to handle glassware. She was so absorbed in the work of welcoming the children and getting them oriented to the space that she didn't notice the bleachers filling up. At eleven o'clock, she looked up from a block tower one child was building and saw that every seat was taken. People were standing at the edges. Teenagers hung off the sides of the upper seats to get a better view.

For a moment, Helen felt like a zoo animal in a room of

smaller zoo animals. But she saw how rapt the crowd was. And the children seemed oblivious. She returned to work.

Helen treated all of the children exactly as she would have in a normal Montessori school. With those who spoke a foreign language, she signed. Whenever she happened to glance at the bleachers, they were completely full.

Later that day, she and Maria had a meal in their hotel room. "It is almost as if the people on the bleachers are watching a baseball game," Helen said. Maria had returned from giving the keynote at the National Education Association conference. Both women were exhausted and exhilarated.

On Monday of the second week of the Glass Classroom, the children served themselves an entire luncheon. They carried hot soup in tureens, served it into small bowls, placed candles on the tables, and lit them. The sight of thirty six-year-olds supping with politeness and civility at a candlelit table so delighted the audience that they broke into applause. Helen, who stood at the head of the table, rarely looked up, but did so in time to see a large feathered hat. It was Maria, sitting among the crowd and clapping along with the rest of the crowd. The two women shared a look of mutual pride.

Two months later, after the Glass Classroom had won two gold medals, Helen and Maria met for dinner in the formal dining room at the Fairmont. Maria gave Helen a small box. Inside was a gold watch.

"I am grateful for your enthusiasm, your grace, and your strength," Maria said. "I have sat in the bleachers watching you work with children. Everything you do is precisely what I would be doing."

Before Helen could say anything, Maria continued. "I will

stay in San Francisco a while longer. Then I will go to Los Angeles to see Mario married to Helen Christy. After that, I will return to Europe. My father is ill. Countries all over Europe want my help in starting Montessori schools, and I must answer their call. My heart is there, and this terrible war asks all of us to do everything we can to achieve peace."

"But there are many people in America who want to create Montessori schools," Helen protested.

"They will change my work, reformulate it," Maria responded. "That seems to be the American way. To continue doing my work my way, I must return to Europe. I don't work with committees." Her voice had an air of finality.

"Then I accept this gift, with gratitude and love," Helen said. "When I look at it, I will think of you and what you have brought to my life and to America. I do believe that any theory or methodology should allow for change, adaptation, and discovery. On that, we differ. And I enjoy working with committees. So I will do my best to carry on your work. But I cannot promise that it will not change."

The two women parted the next day. Maria took the train to Los Angeles and attended Mario's wedding to Helen Christy. She understood that her son needed to create his own life and family. And she belonged at her father's side.

On the night before Maria Montessori left for Europe, she and Mario sat in the garden of the house on Virgil Street, where he and Helen now lived. "I am returning to Europe to open schools and to be with my father," Maria said. "You said to me not long ago that you would come if I needed you.

"I need you. I need your spirit, your heart, and your counsel. I plan to make my home in Barcelona. If you come to Italy, you will be forced into the military. Montessori schools are blossoming in Spain. It is fertile ground for the growth of all that is meaningful to us and our mission. I cannot live forever a continent and an ocean away from my beautiful son."

"I will join you, Mother," Mario answered. "I'll come before too long. We won't be in California forever."

A small voice piped up. "You haven't asked me what I would like to do," Helen Christy, now Helen Montessori, said from the door to the patio.

"We are one family," Mario said. "One mission. We will go where we can do the most good. Right now, we are here with the school in Hollywood. But we won't always be here."

Helen said nothing and closed the door.

The next day, Maria began her long journey back to Italy. Two days after she returned, Alessandro Montessori died. Looking through the leather scrapbooks that lined the shelves of his room, Maria found every article that had ever been written about her. She prayed to God in gratitude for her father, a military man who was willing to change so she could become herself.

Maria's reunion with Anna Maccheroni in Barcelona in the fall of 1916 was delightful. It cemented Maria's decision to move permanently to Barcelona. Maria was impressed by the work Anna had done there. The Catalan government, eager to institutionalize Montessori schools, had provided funds to open a Montessori elementary school as well as a teacher training institute. This gave Maria the opportunity to formalize her teacher training course. She did that at an international training, her fourth, held in Barcelona.

The course enrolled 185 students from all over the world. It was held in a white adobe building in the oldest part of the city.

The thick walls offered a welcome respite from the hot afternoons. The red-tiled floors were cool underfoot, and fountains splashed in peaceful gardens. The grounds also held a small laboratory school where Anna Maccheroni was the director. Maria could take her students there to see her theories in action.

On the first day of the course, an ornate orange-and-blue chair was brought to the front of the room. It was a Catalan tradition and a sign of respect and honor. As a smiling Maria took her place in the chair, a large group of children and adults gathered before her. They began to form a circle to dance the Sardana, a traditional Catalan folk dance. Their raised hands and precise steps were symbols of cultural pride.

Maria clapped and cheered. Children dressed in the traditional costume of red and white presented her with a Catalan flag and a picture of a donkey. Anna told her the meaning of that particular symbol. "Here, a donkey means, strength, courage, and most of all, common sense," she said.

Maria nodded and smiled. "The older I grow, the more important common sense becomes," she thought. Catalan sunshine streamed through the windows. She looked around at the crowd of teaching students from more than thirty countries. She saw the children and adults who had come to make the day a festive event. The power of community and tradition was palpable.

She thought of a similar gathering nearly ten years ago at the first day of the Casa dei Bambini. Back then, nothing had been proven. Now Montessori schools had opened in England, Spain, Italy, Germany, France, Austria, Argentina, Korea, and Japan. Even in America, where skeptics like William Kirkpatrick of Columbia Teachers College were questioning the validity of her methods, legions of parents continued to pursue Montessori education for their children.

THE SOUL OF A LEADER

"I am humbled and honored by your presence here," Maria began. "Many of you have traveled long distances, some in personal danger, to arrive here today. This beautiful building in a peaceful setting, provided to us by the Catalan government, is a reminder to us of what we all yearn for: sunshine, unity and safety.

"We cannot forget that less than six hundred miles from this very spot, in Verdun, France, the horrors of war are taking place at this very moment. Young men are dying and towns are being decimated. Civilians are losing their lives and families are being torn asunder. Orphans by the thousands are being created.

"On this brilliant, happy day here in Barcelona, why am I talking to you about the war? Because I want to tell you of an idea I have had. It is being organized in Paris as I speak. La Croce is a service for refugee children, a way of using the Montessori system to heal the wounds of war and to help bring these traumatized children back to some sense of normalcy. To bring order, for them, to a world that has become chaotic and intolerable through no fault of their own, so healing can begin.

"One day, this war will end. But what kind of world do we, as citizens of the world, want to create? That is why we are gathered here today. We are not training to be teachers. We are training to find the greatest potential in every child here. In each of these encounters, we plant the seed for hope in the world, for a future in which peace is possible for every human being.

"I have just completed my new book. It is called *The Advanced Montessori Method*. It details the application of   the Montessori system to elementary children. These are the building blocks, the individual steps we must take if we are to institute permanent change. Education is the key to peace. And by your presence here, you are at the forefront of a new and bright future for all humankind.

"During this course, you will come to understand how I arrived at my perceptions and the specific application of practical steps as they relate to the physical and intellectual development of the child. Don't take my word for it; you will be able to see this for yourself at the laboratory school on these grounds. Our purpose here is directed at the heart and soul of each child in that school. This is where all of our thoughts, all of our energies, and all of our work must be directed. Then we must direct our life mission to the great work that lies ahead.

"Healing the world through educating the mind and the soul of a child will not always be easy work. But if, as it does for me, it fills your life with purpose and meaning, I invite you to join us on the journey. If one of the foundations of my work is learning through the senses, I invite you to open all your senses, to observe and to allow yourselves to really look and to really see children as they are and as they can be."

As the international group of teachers began the Montessori training course, they were impressed by the students at the laboratory school. The children went about their work with purpose and focus, refusing to be distracted. One visitor who brought in a bag of candy as a reward was shocked when the children showed no interest in it. They were already doing what they wanted. Whatever activity they were doing at the time was, as Maria said, "the correct activity for the precisely correct time in their development." They were not doing it for candy or rewards.

Maria Montessori had reached a pinnacle. When the fourth teacher training ended just before Christmas 1916, her teacher training course had been fully codified. To become a certified Montessori teacher, one had to take fifty hours of classes, observe for fifty hours, student teach for another fifty hours, then pass written and oral examinations given by Maria herself. Maria had been dreaming about this moment for years, and it had finally come.

With Maria's blessing, the students were sent to various parts of the world, presumably to start their own Montessori schools. Anna Maccheroni continued to teach at her school, beloved by the children. Barcelona was welcoming, and the Catalan culture appealed to Maria's sense of pragmatism and spirituality. Yet Maria yearned to have Mario by her side. Without him, she felt a constant emptiness.

In the chapel near the Montessori elementary school, the priest allowed the children to help serve Mass. He was impressed by their concentration and their sense of the sacred. The children looked forward to it as a highlight of their week. This inspired Maria to begin writing a book about children and spirituality. *The Child in the Church* would be published in Naples in 1922 and in London in 1929.

Maria, Anna, the children, and their parents celebrated the end of the war in Europe with a special Mass on November 11, 1918.

On Christmas Eve 1918, Maria and Anna bundled themselves in lamb's wool coats and walked to the chapel along the Gran Via Barcelona, the broad avenue that cut through the city. Colored lights were strewn over the live crèche scene in Sant Jaume Square. Maria saw the Catalan Mary lovingly embrace her baby: not a doll, but a live infant who gazed up at his mother. Maria assumed they were a real mother and child. She was powerfully moved.

As they approached the chapel, the children's choir was singing. The chapel was crowded and festive. Green boughs hung from the rafters and the sweet smell of incense wafted through the air. Maria and Anna found places to sit. As they did, the children's choir began to sing "On December five and twenty, fum, fum, fum, oh a child was born this night . . ."

Suddenly Maria began to cry. It was as though a dam had broken inside her. She couldn't stop. Throughout the service, she wept in fits and starts. Anna was beside herself with worry. The chapel was so crowded there was no possibility of slipping away quietly.

"I am embarrassed to do this in front of my friends, in front of my students," Maria whispered between sobs, "I don't know what has come over me."

The moment the service ended, the congregation began to crowd around Maria. Anna had no idea what they were going to do.

"Forgive her," Anna said. "She has lost both of her parents and misses them very much."

"She cries with us! She feels with us! She is one of us!" exclaimed an old woman wearing a red beret. Maria was besieged with well-wishers who embraced her, kissed her, and invited her to their homes for Christmas dinner. By now, Maria had recovered herself enough to politely but firmly turn down their invitations.

Maria and Anna walked arm-in-arm through the Barcelona streets, returning home to a midnight Christmas dinner. Over duck with roasted chestnuts, Maria said, "They admire me and they are kind to me. But they don't understand me. I am not a sentimental grandma who wants to tell children fairy tales, hug and kiss them, and hand out caramels. I am a serious scientific investigator. I am doing deep and profound work. The work of respecting human nature and allowing children to teach me, to reveal to me their God-given potential. It seems that no matter how long I live, how many times I state it, say it, prove it, it is never enough. Thank God for you, Anna Maccheroni. And Anna Fedeli. And Mario."

"There are many more who understand you, my dottoressa," said Anna. "And the number is growing all the time." She excused herself from the table and came back with an envelope in her hand. "It is a telegram. It came this afternoon from Hollywood in America."

Maria tore it open and read aloud, "Helen and I coming to live in Barcelona. Need house for three. Helen, myself, and grandchild, due in June. Love, Mario."

Chapter Eleven

THE SOUL OF A SCIENTIST

The sky over the Keizersgracht Canal was a cerulean blue backdrop for the white, yellow, and red houses that lined each side. Wooden boats floated placidly at their moorings. Maria Montessori and Caroline Tromp walked along the cobblestone streets, alert to the cyclists passing by. They were going to meet a scientist, Hugo de Vries.

It was May 1919, and Maria was in Amsterdam. Thus far, it was the opposite of what she had experienced in America. The reception was enthusiastic but simple and modest.

The first Montessori school in the Netherlands had opened in 1914. A teacher training institute had followed, begun with Maria's permission and with strict adherence to Montessori principles and theories. A Montessori society was already well established and communicated with Maria often, seeking her advice.

The Montessori method had been institutionalized in the Netherlands in precisely the manner Maria would have wished.

Even during the war, Montessori schools in the Netherlands had flourished. Caroline Tromp, a stout, practical Dutch woman, was in charge. Her combination of passion and pragmatism acted on Maria like a balm.

Caroline was Maria's guide on this visit. On a walk in Amsterdam's Vondelpark, Maria had confessed to Caroline her love of butterflies.

"Then you must meet Professor de Vries!" Caroline exclaimed. "He is a fan of yours and a scientist. I can't explain why I think Maria Montessori should meet a seventy-year-old professor, but there you have it. I sometimes act on Dutch instinct. It has never failed me yet."

They came to a large black door with a knocker in the shape of a butterfly. "Exhibit A," said Caroline with a broad smile. "I am never wrong."

Professor de Vries was a tall, dignified looking man with curly dark hair and bright blue eyes. A silk cravat was tied around his neck. "To what do I owe the pleasure of finding two distinguished women at my door?" he asked, smiling. "Please, come in and have some tea and stroopwafels."

"Stroopwafels are cookies with caramel inside," Caroline told Maria. "A Dutch treat not to be missed." To de Vries, she said, "I have brought my knitting, as I am certain the conversation between you two will go way over my head."

De Vries smiled. "Join me in my garden on this lovely day. Dr. Montessori, this is a great honor."

"The honor is all mine," said Maria.

They walked to the back of the house and out to a garden blooming with poppies. Butterflies were everywhere. Chairs were arranged around a small table. In moments, a tea tray appeared, with cookies.

"I have read your book *Species and Varieties: Their Origin by Mutation*," Maria said. "I have often wondered if many of your ideas about how plants grow might also apply to children. I am especially fascinated by your work with the Porthesia butterfly larvae. I have loved caterpillars and butterflies since I was a child. Their development fascinates me."

"As it should," said de Vries, pouring cups of chamomile tea. "You must have lemon and sugar in your tea. It is good for the digestion. And at least four stroopwafels. If you have enough sugar in your system, a butterfly might land on you."

"I don't believe that for a second," said Maria, "but I'll pretend to as an excuse to eat these cookies."

"A healthy skeptic and a practical woman," de Vries said admiringly. "That's what I like. Now let me explain my idea using the poppy here."

"I am taking out my knitting," said Caroline.

Professor de Vries began. "There is a defined and specific period in which the poppy must decide whether the young stamen will grow out normally or metamorphose into secondary pistils," he said. "It is only a tiny moment in time during which external conditions can produce a corresponding change in the poppy. The whole plant will be affected by this, as once the moment has gone, there is no going back. I call this the sensitive period."

Maria's face lit up. "Children have specific instincts and developmental periods. Or, as you say, sensitive periods. Like caterpillars, who know instinctively how to find the leaves they need to feed themselves, at the far end of the branch, children will go toward what they need if it is there in the environment in the right place at the right time.

"There will be a period of intense focus," she continued. "A cycle of intense involvement with that activity or object. And then it will subside. At that moment, the child is in a restful state. But then that window of opportunity for that piece of development will close, whether the work takes place or not."

"So these periods of sensitivity, for both plants and children, are necessary and essential to their proper development," said de Vries.

"Exactly," Maria said. "When I was a child in Ancona, my mother and I collected larvae and watched them grow into butterflies. My nephew Mario did the same as a boy."

"Your own period of sensitivity, eh?" said de Vries.

"Do adults have these periods as well?" Maria wanted to know. "Because I seem to be focused entirely on these cookies."

Professor de Vries smiled. "Like a caterpillar, you know what is good for you."

Maria sat quietly, enjoying another stroopwafel and the thought of children moving through sensitive periods—for order, for language, even for walking—on their way to becoming beautiful butterflies.

Maria arrived back in Barcelona the evening of June 15, 1919. Mario met her at the station. He was beside himself.

"It's happening!" he exclaimed. "Helen is at the hospital. You must come immediately!"

"Is she all right?" Maria asked, alarmed. "Nothing has gone wrong, I hope?"

"The baby is coming!" he said, as he rushed toward his car. Once they were both inside, he drove crazily through the winding streets, honking loudly at other cars in his way.

"Remember, childbirth is the most natural thing in the

world," Maria said, as calmly as she could. "It has been happening since the world began."

"No lectures, Mother!" Mario warned. "It has never happened to me before. Or to Helen."

"You are right Mario. I apologize. Forgive me."

At the hospital, Mario took his mother's arm, more for his sake than hers, and together they climbed the marble steps to the building. They walked to the second floor, where a nurse greeted them with these welcome words: "Mother and baby girl Montessori are resting well."

Maria and Mario turned to each other. Although taller, Mario laid his head on his mother's shoulder and wept tears of gratitude. Maria held her son tightly and closed her eyes, dissolving into the joy of a new life, a new generation.

"We are going to name her Marilene," he finally said. "It's a combination of Maria and Helen. It means Beloved."

Maria spent a week with them, cooking for them, helping care for Marilene, and tending the garden behind their home in Barcelona.

When Maria Montessori stepped from her train car at Charing Cross on August 30, 1919, one day before her forty-ninth birthday, it seemed as though all of London was there to greet her. There were dignitaries from the British parliament, former students, and the 250 new teacher training students who had been selected from over 3,000 applicants.

Maria stood while flowers were presented and speeches were made. The speakers praised her discoveries, her work with children, and her advancement of rights for women and children. She was grateful that the connection between education and peace was made. Although Maria had grown used to such welcomes, she was always moved by them.

Anna Maccheroni, who had arrived early to attend to details, pushed through the crowd. The sight of her made everything feel right. A woman with dark wavy hair and large round glasses stepped directly in front of Maria.

"I am Sheila Radice, a journalist who—"

"Of course," Maria interjected, smiling. "I know who you are. You are an editor of the *London Times Educational Supplement*. You are so kind to publish my letters and opinions, and you have allowed me to express my ideas to the world. I am indebted to you and your newspaper. May I introduce you to my colleague, Anna Maccheroni? Would you like to share a ride to our hotel? Perhaps you can point out some landmarks."

Sheila, who had hoped only for a brief initial greeting, was delighted to accept the invitation. She was charmed by Maria's lack of pretension. As the car made its way through the streets, Maria noticed the empty lots, the spaces between buildings where nothing stood. There were rooflines that ended abruptly and gaping holes in the ground. There were fronts of buildings with nothing behind them.

The day was hot and gray, and they rode with the car windows open. As they stopped at a corner, Maria saw a young man, a beggar. Half his face was covered with a silver mask.

"That is a veteran who suffered a gas attack during the war," Sheila explained, compassion in her voice. "Signs of the war are everywhere in London, even though it officially ended nine months ago. Rubble from the German bombings has been cleared away, but the deep scars will always be with us."

Maria asked the driver to stop. She got out of the car and

knelt beside the young man. She gave him all the money she had.

They continued on and approached a building where scaffolding surrounded bits of door frames.

"That is Upper North Street Primary, the site of one of the worst bombings. Two years ago, on June 13, 1917, a German zeppelin dropped a bomb on the school at midday, just before lunch. The third floor was for boys, the second floor for girls, and the first floor was for infants. Eighteen children died that day, thirteen under the age of five. Mr. Benjamin Batt was a caretaker at the school," Sheila said, her voice breaking, "and he found his son's body in the rubble. But we are rebuilding the school, and it will open again soon."

Maria and Anna took in the scene and thought of their own classrooms of five-year-olds. They said silent prayers of tribute to the souls lost that day.

Everywhere she looked, Maria saw signs of the war's devastation on the city and its people. Most Londoners wore expressions of grimness mixed with determination. She knew that her own work, and her cadre of 250 teaching students, represented a return of hope after years of darkness.

As Sheila Radice observed Maria Montessori's first speech at St. Bride Foundation in London, she immediately realized how seeing and hearing her in person illuminated her writing. Radice saw that Maria used no notes. She was proposing a way to bring lasting peace to the world through education, and she was doing it seemingly off the top of her head. Maria presented her ideas in ways that appealed to the mind, heart, and values of her listeners. Some were academics and educational theoreticians. Some were curious teachers who left as inspired disciples.

Sheila Radice was further impressed by Maria's stamina and energy. Maria would give a lecture three evenings each week. The topics would include the specific application of materials to primary and elementary students, anatomy, psychology, diet, and philosophy of education. Sheila was amazed by Maria's ability to cross-reference different disciplines.

The teacher training course was now codified. Once students successfully completed the course, they were given a diploma signed by Maria. The diploma stated that they were now able to open schools. It also stated specifically that they were not allowed to train other teachers. Only Maria Montessori could train Montessori teachers.

Maria and Anna stayed in England for nearly six months. During that time, Sheila Radice became a friend as well as a colleague. She was often invited to dinner, where Maria was usually the cook.

"It is something my mother did, and generations before her," Maria said one evening as she prepared that evening's meal. "I believe that when we lose touch with everyday things like cooking, cleaning, and caring for ourselves, we become slaves and not free, forced to depend on someone else to take care of us. Have you ever eaten gnocchi? That is what I am preparing tonight."

"Like many things since you arrived here in England and we became friends, it will be new to me," said Sheila.

"And what has been your favorite new thing?"

"That's easy. Watching you and Anna in the classroom among the children. Seeing so many children all involved in their work, focused on their frames or their counting or balancing, and then seeing you and Anna laughing and enjoying yourselves in the middle of it all. But what do you say to critics who say that your method is not imaginative enough, or William Kirkpatrick from Columbia, who wrote a whole book criticizing you?"

Maria laughed heartily. She was slicing garlic very carefully, very thinly. "I would say this is about translating children's natural impulses into action so they might develop aptitudes that will allow them to paint, write great literature, lead countries, heal bodies. I would say to any skeptic, 'The children are right there, in classrooms all over the world. You can see them if you will put down your pen and pipe, leave your office and go to them.' If they will do this and open their eyes, it is all in front of them."

Finished with the garlic, Maria reached for a handful of carrots. "We have to wait for water to boil so we can cook potatoes to make gnocchi," she said. "We have to slice garlic, parsley, and carrots just so, and add the tiniest amount of sugar, then wine, and don't forget a pinch of nutmeg. Too little and there is no flavor. Too much and it is overly sweet. This is what I love about cooking. You can't rush it. It is a physical, chemical activity.

"So it is with children. There are specific things to be done at specific times. You can't rush them into being. You can't skip steps. So it is with teacher training. You can't add what doesn't belong, rush things, or focus on your own gain and glory instead of on the children."

"Is there anyone you would trust completely at this moment?" asked Sheila, stirring the potatoes in the bubbling water.

"Yes," said Maria, without hesitation. "My nephew Mario."

Maria's final speech in England, given at the Savoy Hotel for the Royal Society of Medicine, was the high point of her time there. As Maria walked onto the stage, she was taken back nearly thirty years to a similar experience. She saw a sea of men, many with their arms crossed, looking at her as if challenging her to prove that she was worthy of their attention. Listening to her introduction, hearing the words "innovator," "feminist," "teacher," "educator," "world-famous," she knew she would begin her speech with the story of the children in the slums of the San Lorenzo.

Dispelling the notion that she was against stories and fairy tales, Maria Montessori lauded England's love of children's literature. She explained that her work with children gave them the foundation for creativity. Without self-reliance, self-discipline, and the ability to organize thoughts, coherence was impossible to achieve. She held her audience rapt for two hours and received a standing ovation.

Maria refused to relent on the notion that she alone was the sole person able to train teachers for Montessori schools. "There is a paradox here, Maria. Don't you see it?" said Sheila Radice as they traveled to the train that would take Maria back to Spain. "You want the child to be fiercely independent, and yet, if I may be so bold, you want to retain iron control over your own methodologies and the people who practice them."

"I see no problem," Maria replied. "The latter will allow the former. There can be no freedom without strict boundaries. I know I am leaving here with a schism between those who support my vision and those who wish to use it for their own purposes, to adapt it as they have tried to do in America. I will fight that with all my being. On a happier note, I have copied down five of my favorite recipes, ones I made for you. Make them often. They will save you from that odious English fish and chips."

Sheila watched her friend walk slowly up the ramp toward the boat at Folkstone. She knew without a doubt that she had spent the past several months in the company of a woman who had the capacity to see the human experience in a new way. Sheila could see that Maria had already begun to change the face of modern education.

As Maria's black skirts flapped in the wind, Sheila also thought that, like many geniuses, Maria seemed at times isolated and lonely. She was admired by legions of people and nearly worshiped by some. But not often understood. There was part of her that always seemed to Sheila to be hidden. Perhaps that was also part of her mystery. Sheila concluded that Maria Montessori's fierce independence was her best asset, and her worst.

Chapter Twelve

THE SOUL OF COURAGE

As Maria Montessori neared the Braschi Palace in Rome, a fierce wind caught the edge of her wool cape. She pulled it closer. Maria was on the street outside the palace. Food stalls offered roasted hazelnuts, fruits and vegetables, and pastries for sale.

Maria saw two young boys near one of the stalls. They couldn't have been more than six years old. They were thin as wisps and had no coats. A taller, dark-haired boy was holding a large slingshot and ordering the smaller boy to stand at the ready. Maria waited to see what would happen next.

The taller boy put a stone in his slingshot and aimed. He pulled back the band with precision and released the stone. It smacked the center of a melon sitting on the fruit stand. The owner of the stand ran out to see what had happened. Meanwhile, the younger boy stole a head of cabbage and three bunches of carrots. He ran back to his partner as fast as his short legs could carry him. The taller boy clapped him on the back with congratulations.

Maria was impressed by their ingenuity in the face of poverty. She was saddened by their need to steal.

It was February 1924, and cold. Maria made her way up the steps of the Braschi Palace. The headquarters of the Fascist party was once a place of great beauty. It had been refurbished to reflect its new purpose. Two years before, in October 1922, Benito Mussolini's Blackshirts had marched through the streets of Rome. Now a large banner with an image of Mussolini obscured the ancient frescoes on the palace. He was smiling.

Maria remembered that smile from the first days of the Casa dei Bambini in Milan. Mussolini had been a journalist then with Milan's Società Umanitaria. The gleaming grin, faintly menacing, hadn't changed. Back then, Maria would never have guessed that Mussolini would one day be the de facto leader of unified Italy.

Giovanni Gentile, a philosopher and old friend of Maria's from her university days in Rome, had urged her to meet with Mussolini. Gentile was now a minister of education. He thought the meeting was in the best interests of Italy's children.

At home in Barcelona, Mario Montessori, who read the international newspapers, was not so sure. He expressed concern over the meeting. He thought about joining her in Italy so he could be there. But Mario had two young children and a third on the way. He had plenty to do in Barcelona. He thought it best to stay home for a while. More and more, Maria had come to rely on his advice. She counted on him to administer the myriad details of her travels, lectures, and teacher training. Helen's resentment was becoming more pronounced.

The Rome of Maria's childhood had changed greatly. The

city had grown much larger. The streets were filled with soldiers in black shirts. Fascist posters and banners hung everywhere. The people seemed fearful and grim.

Maria visited her old friend Queen Margherita, who also thought a meeting with Mussolini was a good idea.

"Do it for the children you see in the streets without education, without a school to attend," the queen said. "Imagine if each of these children were in a Montessori school. With Mussolini's support, that is a possibility, don't you see? It is everything you have ever wanted, right here in your native country. The dream is within your grasp."

These words rang in Maria's head as she was escorted by two young soldiers over the marble floors and through a series of red-carpeted hallways. Soldiers stood at intervals and raised a stiff arm in the Fascist salute. Maria merely nodded to them and noted that many looked as if they had yet to shave.

They came to a huge door that opened as if by magic. Maria found herself in the large office of Benito Mussolini. Although it was daytime, the room was so dark it took Maria's eyes a moment to adjust. A massive fireplace dominated one wall. A desk on a raised platform commanded another.

"You've come at feeding time," a voice said from the shadows. "You must forgive me for not greeting you at the door. Humans can wait, but not a growing cub."

Il Duce was squatting on the floor. He held a large silver tray heaped with pieces of red meat. He was feeding them to a lion cub. The cub was snapping at the meat as Mussolini held it high, teasing the animal before finally dropping it into the cub's huge maw. Its paws were very large, hinting at the size it would reach as an adult.

"A human child has a head that is disproportionately large,

just like the paws of a lion cub," Maria said. "If I had a skull here, I could show you." She knew Mussolini expected her to react with fear or surprise at the sight of the lion cub. She would do neither.

For a moment, Mussolini continued to play roughly with the cub. Then he stood up abruptly. He shouted to the corner of the room, "Come and take him and these things away."

A young woman with blonde hair bobbed in the style of the day stepped forward. She wore a beaded peach-colored dress and diamond earrings. Mussolini pointed to the lion cub and barked, "Take him away. Now. We have work to do."

Wordlessly, the young woman knelt down to put a rope around the cub's neck. He clawed her arm. The gash began to bleed.

"Does she have a name?" Maria asked. "I'd like to help her, and I would like to address her by name."

"She is Margherita Sarfatti, my assistant. She can take care of herself."

"You may have forgotten that I am a medical doctor," said Maria, walking quickly toward the young woman. Maria gently took her arm and said, "Margherita, I am Maria Montessori, and it is a pleasure to meet you. Although I have never treated a scratch from a lion cub, I am almost certain it is not serious. But it will require peroxide and a large bandage."

Maria took a white napkin from a tea tray set in front of the fireplace. She wound it expertly around Margherita's arm. "There. That will do for now. But make certain you get some disinfectant."

"Thank you," said Margherita. She pulled the recalcitrant cub toward the door with one hand and tried to open it with the other. Mussolini stood and watched. Maria rushed to pull it open. The two women's eyes met.

"Take care of yourself," Maria said. Margherita nodded. They both knew Maria was referring to her whole life, not just a gash on her arm.

Maria turned back to Mussolini, who was biting into a sausage that he held like a cigar.

"You are a magnificent woman. Simply magnificent," he said, waving the sausage in the air. He was pacing back and forth in front of the fireplace. "In five minutes, you have shown me your decisiveness, your strength, and your common sense. Everything I have heard about your schools and your students now makes sense to me. You, as a woman, are the pride of Italy. Our mission will be to create a nation of women like you and men like me. Strong, disciplined, proud Italians who put their nation first."

"I am here to change the lives of children," Maria replied calmly. "Children like the ones outside your palace window, who are not being educated." She walked to a large window covered with red velvet draperies. She pulled one aside and pointed to the fruit stand across the street. The two boys were still there, readying themselves to steal again. Mussolini watched their behavior with mild interest. He was infuriated when he observed the theft.

"The little hellions!" he said. "I will have them brought up here, and they will be so terrified they will never think of stealing again!"

"That was not my point," said Maria. "Where you see hooligans, I see precision, the physics with which the taller boy made his slingshot, the planning, the organization, the communication. If those traits could be used for good, there is no telling how far this young man might go."

Mussolini called for an aide, then pointed to the boys by the fruit stand. "Bring the one with the slingshot to me," he growled.

"Redirecting all of that focus to constructive activity would change his life, the life of his community, and potentially the world," said Maria.

In a few minutes, two soldiers roughly escorted the boy into the room. They pushed him forward and he fell to his knees before Mussolini.

"Please don't kill me! Please don't beat me! I will never do it again!" he wailed. His face was streaked with dirt and tears.

"No one is going to kill you or beat you," Mussolini said. "I want you to meet someone. But first, tell me your name."

"Roberto Belli, sir!" said the terrified boy.

"Do you see this lady standing here?"

"Yes, sir."

"Do you know who she is?"

"No, sir."

"She is one of the greatest educators in the world. And she is going to bring education to Italy to change the lives of people like you. As a part of the great Fascist Party, she will create a new future for the children of Italy."

Maria knelt down in front of the boy. She put her hands on his shoulders. He was shaking with fear.

"You have only done what you needed to survive," she said. "But you have so many talents. So many possibilities. I want you to go to school and become the best young man you can be."

She wrapped her cape around him. "There is a school on the Via dei Marsi where you can start tomorrow. I will see to it."

"Feed him something and take him home," Mussolini said, dismissing him.

Roberto tried to return the cape to Maria. She insisted that he keep it.

When he had gone, Maria said, "Education is the key to creating independent, free people."

"You have them reading at three, right?" asked Mussolini, ignoring her comment. "Do you realize how far ahead Italy will be with children who are reading at three? What is the magic trick you have?"

"There is no magic trick," Maria said. "There is only the child's own initiative, combined with the right materials at the right time. And not all of our children read at three. Those are exaggerations that people—"

Mussolini interrupted. "I know all about exaggerations. I also know your results are no exaggeration. Giovanni Gentile, our mutual friend and the great philosopher of the Fascist Party, has told me that for education in Italy, there is no greater person than Maria Montessori. I have inspectors looking at all of your schools, and I am getting some excellent reports."

"You should see for yourself," Maria said. "Come and visit a school."

"I don't have the time. But I have eyes and ears on every street, in every town, and they all tell me to support the great Maria Montessori. The children of Italy will show the world our greatness."

"It is my hope that all children find their God-given potential."

"They will find God in the state, and in their loyalty to their country. Together we will help them. You need a strong man of will to help you. I am that man."

Maria bristled. She stood up and stared directly at Mussolini. They were the same height. "I have created the Montessori system with no one's help and no one's will but my own."

"Of course, my lady," said Mussolini with a grin. "You will be in charge of the road. I am just going to help pave the way so it will be a smooth, bump-free ride. For the glory of Italy."

"For peace on this earth," Maria said.

A knock came at the door. Two officers stepped inside.

"It is time for me to go," said Mussolini. "You will have everything you need."

Maria looked down at the marble floor. She saw several large drops of Margherita Sarfatti's blood.

Mussolini shrugged. "Nothing can grow without a little spilled blood."

Two more men burst into the room, wielding cameras.

"One last thing," said Mussolini. "We must record our meeting for history's sake. Something to commemorate the day when the future of Italy's children took a great leap forward."

He guided Maria to a set of stairs and stood two steps above her so he looked taller. An aide appeared and brushed Il Duce's coat. Someone said, "Smile!" Flashbulbs popped.

"Mussolini lost no time in making use of his relationship with you, and the respect and prestige you have throughout Europe," said Mario later that month as they traveled to Vienna. The photograph and an accompanying article had appeared in all the international papers.

"Giovanni Gentile is a deeply intellectual man and an old friend," Maria said. "As minister of education, he wouldn't ask me to do this unless—"

Mario held up his hand. "Giovanni Gentile is a leading member of the Fascist Party. No matter how intelligent he is, I worry."

"Mario, you know I have always been apolitical. My focus is and always will be on the children. If we want to have a peaceful world, we must educate the next generation of children to be peaceful. This is an opportunity to do so in my own country."

"I wish I could be so sure of myself, Mother," said Mario wistfully. "I am torn all the time between my work with you, which is my life's blood, and Helen and the children."

Their conversation was interrupted as they reached the Austrian border. A bored official with a thin black mustache stepped inside their compartment. When he looked at Maria's passport, he excitedly pulled a newspaper out of his pocket. He pointed to her photo with Mussolini and snapped into the Fascist salute. Maria gave him a tight smile he seemed to take as approval. He backed out, grinning broadly.

Both Maria and Mario were impressed by the work that Lili Roubiczek, a Viennese teacher, and her associate Lisl Herbatschek had done in opening a Montessori school in Vienna. With virtually no funding, they had used their youthful zeal to help change the lives of poor children in Vienna. They had gone against the disapproval of their own families and endured financial hardship, even sleeping at the school, to completely commit to Montessori principles. The result was a flourishing school with a roster of students from many nations and economic backgrounds.

Liesl Herbatschek, musically gifted and barely out of her teens, had incorporated music into the curriculum. Maria approved and the two became close friends. Maria was touched by the sacrifice and hard work of the two younger women. She recognized in them the same kind of vision she had at their age.

~

An international Montessori conference in Denmark at Elsinore Castle in 1929 gave Maria an opportunity to speak to the global community. From the ramparts of the castle, she addressed a crowd that included people from forty-three nations.

"I cannot stand here without thinking of the noble Hamlet, a young man who refused to accept the status quo and who searched for truth and sought justice for wrongs. We are gathered here at a time when the world seems poised for change. Many of you are reformers and wish to see a different kind of world, one without violence, war, and destruction.

"I was born in Italy and took my medical degree there. I began developing my theories of education, always based on the observation of actual children, at the Casa dei Bambini in Rome. I have spent the balance of my life in almost constant motion, overseeing the opening of schools and lecturing in America, England, Germany, France, Austria, and most recently in South America.

"Caroline Tromp in the Netherlands has led the organization of primary, elementary, and even secondary schools in that country. I am currently working in my native country to establish a nationwide Montessori school system. In recent years, the teachers I have trained in many countries have taken over the classroom work while I have continued to lecture. Increasingly, my focus is on creating a peaceful world.

"It stands to reason that the seed for this is with our children, in how we treat them and how they are educated. My work, which has been carefully developed over forty years of observation of children and how they grow, is specifically calibrated to what I call 'sensitive periods.' The materials I have developed to go along with them must be used scientifically and introduced at the appropriate time. Only teachers who have been personally trained by me are qualified to do this.

"You come from forty-three different countries. I can tell you this much after observing children on many continents: they are all alike in wanting to love and be loved, in wanting to develop and grow and reach toward the light, toward the fulfillment of their own potential. They must do so in their own way and on their own timeline. If their rights and freedoms are respected and encouraged, mankind will continue to develop science and technology that will create, not destroy.

"We must all begin to realize that nationalism is not the answer. We all live together on this planet. And we must educate children to access their self-determination, compassion, and free will. This is our job, our duty, and our calling as teachers, leaders, parents."

After the speech, a reporter asked, "How does all this freedom you talk about square with the repression and cruelty of the current Fascist regime in Italy?"

Maria gazed at him with serene, dark eyes and responded, "I am apolitical. My only concern is for the rights and the freedom of children. All children, for their future and the future of the world. I repeat. I am apolitical."

The speech and her answer were widely reported. They did not sit well with Benito Mussolini.

As the new decade began, Montessori schools continued to be established in Italy under the Fascist regime. They produced measurable success. Military families, among many others, clamored to enroll their children.

Mussolini and the Opera Montessori, the administrative arm of the schools, organized a grand opening for a teacher training for 100 students. At the senatorial palace, Maria stood before a large Roman statue for a lengthy photo session. As she looked out at the crowd of students from all over the world, the thought of celebrating the permanent establishment, in her own country, of what she had begun more than twenty years before filled her heart with joy.

She also saw the Blackshirts who lined the periphery of the crowd. She saw the Fascist flags snapping in the wind. She began her speech by saying, "I believe education can help mankind triumph over evil, over hatred, over the propensity for war." Several Fascist officials shifted uncomfortably in their front-row seats.

This first international training course in Italy was a happy time for Maria. Mario had established, with Maria's approval, a headquarters in Amsterdam for the world Montessori movement. It was called the Association for Montessori International. From this hub, communication and information about the publication of books and the availability of materials all became centralized. Mario was now her partner and most trusted advisor in all things. By the mid-1930s, Montessori schools in the Netherlands were well established.

One afternoon in April 1934, Maria sat quietly on the patio of her home in Barcelona. Her sewing kit was out. She was repairing a hole in one of her aprons. It had belonged to Renilde. Mario had come for a rare visit. With four children, a wife, and his own responsibilities in organizing and supporting his mother's work, the chance to sit together had become increasingly rare.

Maria had just returned from Italy, where she was working

with the Fascist government to establish Montessori schools nationwide.

"You are never idle, are you?" said Mario, laughing and shaking his head.

"I am practicing the freedom to care for myself," Maria countered with a broad smile.

"It is a lovely afternoon. But, as Winston Churchill of England says, a storm is gathering, and it will affect us all. I have been reluctant to tell you this, but Franco has withdrawn official support for Montessori schools in Spain. I received the letter yesterday, while you were traveling back from Italy."

Maria clipped the thread and carefully tied a tiny knot behind the patch on the apron. She held up the apron. Where there had been a hole, there was now a series of undiscernible stitches. She folded the apron into a neat square and gazed at her son.

"The children in our schools and their families have come to depend on us. Can we not continue regardless of government support? After all, we started without it."

"Times have changed," said Mario. "We could continue, yes. But the gathering storm includes this country, Franco's Spain, where we live, where my children and wife live. We are under martial law. Assassinations are taking place every day. Italy just invaded Ethiopia. These are perilous times."

Maria took her son's hand. "Of course I always want to know the truth. I respect your thoughts, as you know. But we have lived through perilous times before, have we not?"

"You have been focused on your work here and in Italy, so you haven't seen this," said Mario. He opened his briefcase and retrieved a copy of a Berlin newspaper, the *Berliner Tageblatt*.

On the front page was a photograph of Maria Montessori being burned in effigy over a pile of her books.

"The Nazis have closed all of your schools in Germany. Another war is coming. I don't know the answer for us. But I do know that Churchill is right."

On a sunny day in May 1934, Maria Montessori visited a school not far from the Braschi Palace. As she passed the home of the Fascist party, she glanced at the banner with Mussolini's image. It covered an entire wall of the building and had grown even more menacing.

Now sixty-four and very matronly, Maria sat in the middle of the schoolroom on a child-size chair. Dressed in the voluminous black skirt she wore despite changing fashions, she remained an energetic figure, still taking notes, still observing the children with care and wonder.

There was a knock at the door. A soldier stepped inside. He gave the Fascist salute and strode toward Maria. He handed her a letter with an official seal. Then he gave her a parcel wrapped in brown paper.

She looked into his young face and recognized his features, despite his blank expression. She opened the parcel first. It was the wool cape she had given to a six-year-old boy ten years earlier.

"I know you," said Maria.

His face relaxed, and he leaned toward her. "I am Roberto Belli. I wanted to return your cape one day. I never forgot your kindness. I have been educated at Montessori schools since the day we met."

He lowered his voice. "I didn't want to join the army, but I had no choice. Now I have promised to serve my country."

Another solider entered the room and stood beside the door. Roberto straightened. His voice grew louder and more strident. "I am a second lieutenant in the Army of the Italian Republic. Il Duce is my leader. I was deputized to deliver this letter to you. And wait for an answer."

"Please, Roberto. Make yourself comfortable," said Maria, breaking the seal on the letter. Reading it gave her a moment to compose herself. She was remembering the quaking boy from ten years ago. He was now a solider in the Fascist army of Mussolini. Montessori schools had not saved him from a fate that was decided by the leadership of his country. She was shocked and profoundly dismayed.

The letter was signed by Mussolini himself. It stated that all schools in Italy needed to clothe their students in approved Fascist uniforms. It further stated that only Fascist party songs and curriculums specifically approved by the Fascist party were to be taught. It went on to delineate a long list of regulations, ending with the requirement for all teachers and students to use the Fascist salute. The last line specified immediate compliance, with no exceptions.

Maria looked up from the letter. Roberto was talking quietly with a young boy who was building a block tower. Ida and Rosaria were tracing sandpaper letters. Marco was blindfolded and Gino was testing him on his balance. All over the large, bright room, children were actively engaged and focused.

Maria knew she could not agree to any of the demands in the letter. She also knew that would mean the end of her work in Italy. It would mean the end of any support for Montessori schools.

She would return to Spain. She would continue to travel the world on behalf of the children. But what would happen to these children? To Ida and Rosario, Marco and Gino? Would they grow up and into a world with increasing technology for destruction? Would they have a hand in creating it? In using it?

Taking pen and paper, Maria wrote a quick and decisive reply to Mussolini's letter. She folded it, slid it into an envelope, sealed it, and handed it to Roberto.

"Here is my answer," she said. "But I will tell you, face to face, that I have never allowed anyone to dictate to me how the Montessori classroom functions. I will not begin now. It would desecrate my vow to do what is in the best interests of the child. Nothing demanded in this letter is in the best interests of the child.

"We must all honor our commitments. Mine are to the children of the world. All of the world. Not just Italy. Yours is to serve your country. May God bless you and protect you."

Maria looked into his eyes and put her hands on his shoulders, as she had done once before so long ago. He moved as if to embrace her. For a moment, she saw the terrified eyes of the six-year-old Roberto. Then he stiffened, gave the Fascist salute, and was gone. The other soldier followed him out the door.

Maria spent the rest of the day among the children. She hugged each one as they left and blessed them. The next day, all Montessori schools in Italy were officially closed.

Maria Montessori sat on her Barcelona patio on a hot afternoon in July 1936. Her doctor and Mario had begun to insist that she take an afternoon nap.

"I am sixty-six, not ninety-six!" she protested when they first proposed it. "I am in perfect health. I made dinner from scratch for thirty people just last night. I have spent the entire year traveling, even to South America. I would be traveling now were it not for Franco's restrictions."

Mario and her doctor were so adamant that she finally acquiesced. She told them she was resting. But she never rested. She used the time to read the final proofs for the reissues of her books *The Mass Explained to Children* and *The Secret of Childhood*. She laughed to herself as she thought of Mario's recent comment, "When do you write? I never see you do it. I only see you lecturing or teaching or traveling or cooking for us all."

She loved sneaking a box of chocolates out to the patio, with a pitcher of cold lemonade. Working on her books, eating a little chocolate, and sipping lemonade, she was contented. Mario would never be the wiser.

She heard voices below her patio and realized they were those of Mario and Helen. They sounded angry. Maria tried to block out their words, as she knew instinctively it was a private conversation.

"We are putting our children at risk to stay here," Helen was saying. "You have two teenagers, an eleven-year-old and a seven-year-old. They all know what is going on and they are frightened. Spain is on the verge of a civil war. Do you put the welfare of the children in the Montessori schools above that of your own?"

"Helen, it isn't as easy as that," Mario said. "You are only thinking of yourself. We have a commitment to the children in these schools. I am in daily touch with the British consulate. They will let us know when they can or should get us out. I am doing all that I can."

Helen's voice rose to a wail. "I am tired of living this way, do you hear me? I am tired of it!"

Maria walked from the patio into her room. She shut the door. Suddenly there was a loud knock on her bedroom door.

"Mammolina, it is Anna. The sailors are here." Anna Maccheroni used the name those close to Maria called her.

Maria opened the door. "Sailors? What sailors?"

"The sailors from the British consulate. They are from a ship that is going to take us to London. They say it is time to go."

"Have you told Mario and Helen?" asked Maria.

"They were talking. I didn't want to disturb them."

"We must disturb them now. How long do we have?"

"They said one hour."

"An hour?" asked Maria incredulously.

"Yes. We can take only small suitcases. Oh, Mammolina, all your manuscripts, all of your beautiful things!" Anna gazed around the room, filled with mementos and photographs.

"Nonsense. There is no time for tears over material things. We have all that we need in our brains. We have our health. My tears are for the people of Spain."

Maria went to find Mario and Helen. "Gather Marilene, Mario Jr., Rolando, and little Renilde. We are leaving Barcelona on a British transport in an hour. With one small suitcase each." Mario and Helen were momentarily stunned. They rushed off to collect as much of their lives as they could.

In precisely fifty-eight minutes, two black cars arrived to take the Montessoris and Anna to board the *HMS Cornwall*, a British light cruiser. The children were fascinated by the display of military might, the gun turrets, and the sailors standing at attention. They momentarily forgot they had left behind nearly everything they owned.

As daylight began to fade and the adrenalin stopped

pumping, the whole family stood on deck and watched Barcelona and their former life disappear from view.

Little Renilde put her hand into her grandmother's hand. "What did you bring?" she asked.

"My two manuscripts, my hopes for the future . . . and you, my beloved," answered Maria.

"I brought this, even though Mamma said I shouldn't," said Renilde. She showed Maria a jelly jar. Inside was a caterpillar forming a chrysalis.

"Ahhh! New life, reaching for the light. Nothing could be more beautiful."

"You won't tell?"

"Not a soul. It will be our secret." Maria's three other grandchildren gathered around. Their faces were golden in the setting sun as they looked out to sea.

"I have everything in the world that is really important to me right here," said Maria. "But I also brought something else." She took out a napkin and unfolded it. Inside were four chocolates.

"One for each of you," she said. "With hopes, dreams, and chocolates, we are unstoppable." She put her arms around her grandchildren.

"Mammolina, will our friends in Barcelona be all right?" asked Marilene.

"I can't truthfully tell you," said Maria, "I wish I could. But I do know that as long as war persists, I will work for peace. Our resolve must be strengthened, not diminished. Always, we must believe there is a way to create a lasting peace, even in the darkest times. We are fortunate to be able to escape. This gives us more responsibility to make the world a better place for those who can't. To change the world so that every child will be safe and free."

A sailor approached the Montessori family and saluted them. He said in halting Spanish that the Admiral would very much like Maria Montessori to address the entire ship.

"What shall I tell them?" Maria asked her gathered grandchildren.

"You can thank them for keeping us safe and free," said Mario Jr.

"What a strong sentiment," said Maria. "That is exactly what I shall do."

Chapter Thirteen

THE SOUL OF RESILIENCE

Although the Montessori family had no definite plans for a new home when they arrived in England, many friends and supporters offered suggestions and invitations. Helen, exhausted by the trip and disoriented by London, was grim and unhappy. Maria, with her characteristic stamina and resilience, went immediately to Oxford to lead a fifth international Montessori congress.

With Mario at her side, Maria presented her idea for what she called "cosmic education," a way to develop the whole person while emphasizing the interconnectedness of all things. At Oxford, and again at the Sorbonne in Paris in 1938, Maria spoke of creating peace through education. The listeners, leaders and educators from all over the world, who saw the coming strife, were eager to hear her message of a hopeful future when the present seemed increasingly dismal.

A contingent of participants from India attended the Oxford congress. They met with Maria and invited her to their country. Leaders from India, a nation of 400 million people and an illiteracy rate of nearly ninety percent, were struck by her combination of spirituality and practicality. They felt that her way of working with children would appeal to the population.

Ada Pierson also attended the conference at Oxford. The daughter of a Dutch banker, she was a vivacious young woman of twenty-four who had completed a Montessori teacher training. She was devoted to Maria, Mario, and the family and empathized with their refugee status.

Ada invited the Montessoris to live at her family estate in the idyllic town of Baarn in the Netherlands. They gratefully accepted her offer. In late fall 1936, the family moved to Baarn. The estate was large enough to house them all comfortably. The rolling green pastures and peaceful setting gave them a needed respite from all they had left behind.

Mario and Maria were still considering the invitation to India. One day, as they sat going over notes for Maria's next book, *God and the Child*, Helen appeared.

"I know you are working. But I feel I must speak with you both." Maria and Mario exchanged glances and put down their papers.

"I believe in your mission, your purpose in life," Helen went on. "It has never wavered or changed since the day I met you, Mario. I just can't be a part of it anymore, or of this marriage. I wasn't made to live like this. You are extraordinary people, both of you. I will live here in the Netherlands to be near my children, who are my world. But I will no longer live with you, Mario.

"Mammolina, I sympathize with the loss of your child during his own developmental years. You are making up for it now. But there is no place for me here. Mario, I will always be the mother of Marilene, young Mario, Rolando, and Renilde. I will always respect you. But I will no longer be your wife. We have been growing apart for years."

Mario hung his head in sorrow.

"Please don't be sad or sorry," Helen said. "We have four beautiful children. They are strong and loving. As Mammolina always says, there is no time for tears, there is much work to be done. It is a relief to me to say this."

Maria remained silent out of respect. There was a long pause. Then she spoke.

"Sometimes we have our goals and missions so firmly in our sights that we forget to see the people right in front of us. I have never for a moment taken your care of the precious children for granted. There were many times when I envied your closeness to them as they were growing. It's true that I didn't have that with Mario, and my heart will always ache for that loss. And I can't say the work we do is easy on a family. I know it isn't."

"We will all survive," said Mario, with conviction and emotion. "And we will thrive. And we will keep on with our work. You are right, Helen. We have grown apart. May God bless you for your courage and your honesty.

"We have found in Laren, not far from here, a building to serve as a laboratory school. There will be several houses nearby. Perhaps we can all put down an anchor there. It can serve as a home base, once more, for the extended family."

Maria was almost seventy years old. Her son was forty-one. They had spent the last twenty-five years working together, traveling together, looking toward the future with determination and hope. They had never wavered in their shared mission, and with the world on the verge of war once more, they wouldn't now.

They accepted the invitation to India. It seemed the perfect way to continue their pursuit of changing the world through education.

The Montessori school in Laren was established, along with nearly two hundred other Montessori schools throughout the Netherlands. When Mario and Maria made their final stop at the school before departing for India, they visited a class of elementary Montessori students.

One young girl with curly dark hair and warm brown eyes brought Maria a bouquet of flowers. "We wish you a wonderful trip to India," the girl said. "I want you to know that, like you, I believe there is good and potential in everyone."

Maria looked into her shining eyes. "What is your name, my dear?"

"Anne Frank," she said with a wide smile.

Maria should have been exhausted. It was late October 1939. The journey from London to Madras had taken three full days, with stops and delays.

World War II had begun on September 1, 1939, with the Nazi invasion of Poland. There was consternation about leaving. But the children seemed happy and settled in Laren. They had encouraged their grandmother and father to go to India, saying they knew it would be good for the children there.

Maria was proud of them for this. Their mother and the entire Pierson family had promised to take good care of them. The trip would include a three-month teacher training in Adyar and three more months of lecturing and traveling in India.

Maria couldn't wait for the small plane to land. The moment the propellers stopped spinning, a ramp popped down. A tall, impossibly slender man with white hair and a huge smile cracked open the door. He was carrying a garland made of orchids that he promptly hung around Maria's neck. He hugged her. He moved energetically and filled the air with words.

"I am K Sankara Menon, and I am here, with all of India, to welcome you. A new era in education, in self-rule, in self-reliance, has begun with the arrival of Maria Montessori in India.

"By some madness, Dr. George Arundale, who is the president of the Theosophical Society, and his lovely wife, the famous dancer Rukmini Devi, have made me headmaster of the school there. They actually think I am fit for the role. Can you imagine? If you'll have me, I will be your assistant while you are here. I may make you crazy. But I will never make you bored.

"And this must be Mario," he said, turning next to him. "The two of you are obviously cut from the same cloth. But here I am, prattling on, and you must be fatigued. Come, come." He took Maria by the arm and helped her down the ramp.

It was twilight. The air enveloped Maria like a warm blanket. Distant sounds of the city became louder as they neared Madras. There were people everywhere, walking beside their car, walking in front of their car. They proceeded slowly as animals and men with pushcarts made their way down the winding streets. The carts were filled to bursting with produce, clothing, and burlap sacks stuffed with rice.

The cacophony in the center of the city was a wall of sounds neither Maria nor Mario had ever before heard. There were high-pitched, flute-like instruments, clanging drums, and street vendors pitching their wares. Above it all was the melodious sound of a foreign language.

Maria noticed a vendor dipping a ball on a stick into a syrupy liquid. "May I try that?" she asked.

"Oh, we must," said K Sankara Menon, stopping the car.

The vendor bowed low at the sight of the foreign woman dressed in black. He dipped the item in the liquid. A circle formed around Maria. Two women stepped forward to offer napkins. Maria graciously accepted. The ball was sweet and spicy at the same time, bursting in her mouth with an exotic taste sensation.

"What is it?" Maria asked with wonder.

"It is Gulab Jamun," Menon said. "India's favorite street food. You may now call yourself a native."

Back in the car, they crossed over the Adyar River, and the noise abruptly ceased. Maria looked out at the river and saw that one bank had very few buildings while the opposite bank was crowded with them.

"Rivers in India are sacred," Menon said, noticing Maria's interest. "We see them as living things, as goddesses. Water is a purifier, and we save one bank for sacred sites. And now we are nearing the grounds of the Theosophical Society, where I am sure you will want to go directly to your rooms and rest."

"Not a bit of it," said Maria. "I am so excited I don't think I'll sleep for days."

The entrance to Madras, the feelings she had experienced since landing, were all brand new. Maria Montessori had never been to India, but she immediately felt at home.

"Please take me on a tour of the grounds," she said. "I can rest anytime."

They were just passing beneath the blue archway to the Theosophical Society grounds. These words were etched into the archway: "There is no religion higher than the truth."

"Years ago, when I had just begun Casa dei Bambini, I met your founder, Annie Besant," Maria said. "I was deeply moved by her stance on women's rights and her fearless leadership of the strike at the match factory in England, which led to better working conditions for thousands of women. Her description of Theosophy, with the idea of tolerance without distinction of race, creed, or color, was so revolutionary it inspired me."

Menon nodded in appreciation. "As Theosophists, we believe that within every human being is a light, a consciousness to be purified. Everything here at the center in Adyar, which was founded by Madame Helena Blavatsky and Colonel Henry Steel Olcott, is meant to reflect the spirit of tolerance.

"Self-reliance and independence are deeply important tenets of our faith. And that is why we have brought you here. In India's struggle for home rule and independence, education is key. Ninety percent of our population is illiterate. One day, we will free ourselves from British rule. But how will we govern as free people without education?"

Menon turned the car into a wide lane covered with an archway of green. Calico flowers and magnolia trees perfumed the air. Water lilies floated in small ponds.

Positioned between the Adyar River and the Bay of Bengal, the grounds of the Theosophical Society, where Maria and Mario were to teach and live, covered nearly two hundred acres. Coconut and casuarina plantations, fruit orchards, temples, and shrines dotted the landscape. Egrets and pelicans stood on the riverbank.

The headquarters hall at the end of the road was a nineteenth-century mansion. As Maria and Mario stepped inside, they found themselves in a large domed central plaza. On the walls were symbols of all of the world's religions. Portions of the wall opened to the outside, where foxgloves, hollyhocks, gladioli, and fuchsia grew in profusion. With the twilight shadows falling into the room, the effect was entrancing.

Maria took Mario's hand, and they leaned against each other as if to confirm that all of this beauty was real.

Continuing their journey around the grounds, they saw that the Theosophical Society practiced what it preached. There was a Buddhist shrine, a mosque, a Hindu temple, a synagogue, a Catholic church, and even a Zoroastrian temple. All of these places of worship were set into groves of ancient trees. In the dwindling light, fruit bats began to appear, and the resonant hum of cicadas began.

The highlight was the ancient banyan tree whose branches grew into the ground, holding up the trunk in a never-ending cycle of mutual dependence.

The tour finished at a limestone two-story bungalow with a spiral staircase on the outside.

"This will be your home while you are here," said K Sankara Menon. "There is a bedroom and study for each of you. If you climb to the roof, there is a view of the Adyar, and you can see all the way to the Bay of Bengal. If you are lucky, tomorrow morning you will see pink flamingos wading in the river's shallows."

Maria couldn't remember a time when she hadn't spent several hours at her desk before retiring. On the first night of her arrival in India, she fell into a deep and restful sleep almost at once. The next morning, a soft chime woke her.

It was six o'clock. She had slept for fourteen hours. Her luggage had been unpacked. Several white cotton gowns trimmed with gold and blue braid were laid across the footstool next to the bed. A quiet knock at the door brought a young woman with a tray of tea. Maria looked out her window and saw sprays of brilliant red and yellow flowers.

"Dottoressa, we have brought you clothing that might help

you to stay cool during our hot days here in India. Breakfast is communal and is ready at the main house."

"What are the beautiful flowers I see outside my window?" Maria wanted to know.

"Those are the flowers of the fire tree. My name is Mina. Dr. Arundale and his wife, Rukmini, are waiting to take you to your opening lecture. That is, once you have eaten."

George Arundale, the president of the Theosophical Society, was indeed awaiting Maria's arrival. He rose to greet her as she walked down the stairs.

"I see you have adopted our native dress," he said. "Very becoming, and very sensible. It is beyond an honor to have you here. When we extended the invitation, we didn't know if some-one of your maturity would want to make the trip."

Maria laughed. "You mean an old woman of nearly seventy? The possibilities that await us give me courage and strength."

Dr. George Arundale was an American who had become a Theosophist and moved to India to take over the presidency of the society. He met and married Rukmini Devi, scandalizing Indian society. He was a Theosophist and a Catholic bishop; she was a Hindu. At the time of their marriage, in 1920, he was forty-two and she was sixteen.

The morning sun dappled the path they walked to the building where Maria would be teaching. "There were so many applicants we had to construct a new building just for this. And even then, we had to turn many away," said Dr. Arundale.

They reached a large, hut-like structure with a roof of palm leaves. Three hundred students sat on straw mats. They wore saris of many colors. To Maria, they looked like hundreds of flowers in bloom.

The students waited expectantly. K Sankara Menon stepped to the center to introduce Maria.

"In theosophy," he began, "we place our trust in great masters, when we find them. Great souls we feel have reached an altered state of existence. Who possess a kind of knowledge that, if we can learn from it and heed it, will change the course of our lives, our children's lives, and the life of our country. Theosophy, as we know, means divine wisdom. There was never a human with more divine wisdom than Maria Montessori."

Several students rose and brought forth a garland made of white orchids. They placed flowers on a table in front of Maria. This would be a daily ritual.

That day, and the next three months, as Maria continued teacher training and started the laboratory school, were revelatory. She took a long time to understand why. Then one day Maria realized that her ideas and theories had been accepted by her students and by the Indian people. The element of struggle, of continually having to prove herself and answer critics, was gone. In its place, she had the time to observe and work.

She was able to observe hundreds of babies and infants. In India, they were not tucked away in nurseries but were part of daily life with their mothers and families. Maria began writing a book about infants and prepared a series of lectures based on her findings.

Maria and Mario conducted the teacher training at the Theosophical Society in Adyar. In late February 1940, at the conclusion of the course, they issued three hundred teaching certificates. They had been visited during the course by some of India's most distinguished leaders including Mahatma Gandhi and Rabindranath Tagore, the only Indian poet to win a Nobel prize. Maria and Tagore became close friends.

Immediately following the course, Maria and Mario traveled to Kodaikanal, Karachi, and Ahmedabad. They crisscrossed the vast country of India under conditions that would have made many people half Maria's age hesitate. She remained full of energy and more determined than ever to bring her ideas for education to the Indian people. They repaid her with devotion, acceptance, and a deep conviction that her work would create better lives for the masses.

In early June 1940, Maria and Mario were preparing to leave India and return to the Netherlands. Mario would make one final trip to Kodaikanal, about five hundred miles from Adyar, before going back to Europe.

On the afternoon of Mario's departure for Kodaikanal, Maria said casually, "I have noticed piles of letters to Ada Pierson waiting to be mailed."

"Yes," said Mario with a smile and a slight blush. "I write to her daily. To let her know about the progress we are making here in India."

"Daily?" Maria teased. "And I have noticed that she also writes to you each day. You'll need a trunk just to carry all those letters."

"She keeps me informed about my children," said Mario.

"Hmmm. Yes, the children. All four of the children. Very important. I love Ada. She is very kind to write to you every single day. About your children."

"I love Ada, too," Mario said, then caught himself. "I mean, I love her dedication. Her hard work."

"Of course," said Maria, having confirmed what she thought was happening. "Now travel safely to Kodaikanal. Give my regards to the teachers there. When you return, we will leave for home, where you can tell all your stories to Ada in person. I will miss the beauty and peace of this place. But we have work to do in Europe."

"On a serious note, some of the news in Ada's letters is very disturbing," Mario said.

"I don't doubt that for a moment. The tolerance and peace we have found here is a taste of what is possible. But there is so much to be done. I know the suffering is only beginning in Europe, and I fear for our Jewish friends and students in particular.

"Even here, revolution is coming. Soon the yoke of British rule will no longer be tolerated. But we will have time to talk about all these things when you return and we travel home. I always feel like I can solve the problems of the world with you by my side. And, of course, Ada."

Mario hugged his mother tightly. "I won't be gone long. And we will dig into the world's problems together."

Maria watched her son walk down the wide pathway outside their bungalow. Like his mother, Mario had taken on native dress while in India. He wore rumpled khaki shorts and a loose-cut shirt. She considered her own salmon-colored sari and reflected on the inward and outward changes she had experienced during eight months in India.

"It is amazing what growth, what confidence, what happiness can take place when one knows they are accepted and loved," Maria mused. "It accelerates the growth of every cell, every particle of one's being." If she had given much to the Indian people, they had given much to her as well.

A week later, on June 10, 1940, Maria was working with Mina to pack her trunk. Mina, who belonged to a lower caste, had joined the teacher training course at Maria's insistence and was hoping to teach at a Montessori school in Kodaikanal. She had become devoted to her Mammolina.

K Sankara Menon appeared at Maria's door. She could tell from his face that something was terribly wrong.

"Dottoressa, there is a British officer at the door downstairs," Menon said. "He has very bad news. Italy has declared war on Britain. He says you are now, as an Italian citizen, an official enemy alien. You must be confined to these grounds by order of the British consulate. It is shameful, but there is nothing we can do."

Maria remained calm. She stood up and thanked Menon for coming to tell her himself. She walked down the narrow steps of the bungalow to the sitting room, where a British officer wearing a white pith helmet and white gloves stood at attention.

"Your country of origin, the one from whence your passport is issued, has declared war on Britain," the officer announced. "I hereby inform you that you are now considered an enemy alien. Your movements will be restricted, as well as the movements of other Italians in this country. Mario Montessori, whom we understand is in Kodaikanal, is now considered an enemy alien. He will be confined in Kodaikanal until further notice. Do you understand?"

He rattled off his sentences with the precision and rapidity of a Gatling gun. Maria remained calm until the final two sentences. The knowledge that Mario would be confined indefinitely in a city five hundred miles away was too much to bear. She sank into a nearby armchair.

"Good God, man!" said Menon. "Do you know who you are talking to? This woman has worked tirelessly on behalf of children, all children, for the past fifty years. She is known the world over."

"There is a war on," the officer said. "She is an Italian citizen and therefore an enemy alien. Those are my orders. There is no exception." With a click of his heels, he was gone. The sound of his boots echoed in the hallway.

Menon turn to Maria, who sat staring straight ahead. "There are people suffering everywhere during this war," she said, as if to herself. "Families are being torn apart, cities destroyed. Children are losing their parents. It only strengthens my resolve. Yes. My resolve is strengthened." She looked up at Menon. "I am hoping I can at least communicate with Mario. It looks as though we are going to be here a long time."

A week later, Maria received a letter from Mario.

Dear Mother,

I look out each day at the mountains of Kodaikanal. The mist hangs over them until the first rays of sun turn them purple, blue, then green. I am surrounded here by people who want to learn what I have to teach, what you have given me. I plan to make the most of it.

I know you have come to depend on me, and you think you need me. But you were strong and purposeful and changing the world before I came along. You will continue to do so. I am with you, as always, in spirit. And if any letter whatsoever can leave here and make its way to Europe, Ada will receive a marriage proposal. A written one, to be followed soon (I hope) by a proposal in person.

She loves you, as do I, and once this war is over and we are all together, we will work as a team, Ada, you and I. I have no doubt of this.

God bless you, Mother dear.

With love,

Mario

K Sankara Menon, George Arundale, and his wife Rukmini Devi spent all of August 1940 planning a seventieth birthday celebration for Maria. Her teacher training students wrote songs and choreographed dances. There were letters and cards from all over the world. Gifts, including a portrait of Gandhi, were given.

Wearing a light blue sari, Maria sat, the center of attention, looking around at her young students. All were now ready to go out into India and begin their own schools. Then the lights dimmed.

Menon said, "We have one last guest who will honor us, due to the graciousness of the viceroy."

The lights went out, candles were lit, and Mario appeared in the archway of the door directly across from where Maria was seated. She rubbed her eyes and thought for a moment that she was imagining things.

Loudly and clearly, Menon said, "We have returned your son to you."

For the first time since his birth, Mario was publicly acknowledged as the son of Maria Montessori. All the years of separation, the years of having to hide, were contained in that moment. Then the son walked into the arms of his waiting mother. The crowd surrounded them, joining hands in a circle. Together they sang the new song by Rabindranath Tagore.

Oh, remember me if I travel far
If old love is covered in tangles of new love
If I am near
If you cannot see me like a shade I remain on
Oh, remember me if tears come on your eyelid
If play stops in the still of honey-like night
If in tears and if you see me not from the corners of your eyes
Yet still remember me.

Chapter Fourteen

THE SOUL OF THE FUTURE

Maria Montessori was gathering up teaspoons and butter knives. "Your silver needs polishing," she said. "Get me a rag and some baking soda and I'll have it done in no time."

Her two young assistants, Catherine Pomeroy and Elizabeth Braun, were dumbfounded. Then they began to laugh. They realized polishing the silver was as much Mammolina as last night's demonstration of how to eat spaghetti. "Anything worth doing is worth doing well," she had reminded them with a grin, taking a large bite of perfectly rolled spaghetti.

Maria was serious about the silver. Catherine ran to get the rag and baking soda.

"Thank you," Maria said. "Now the two of you can tell me all about yourselves while I bring out the shine in these utensils. It's been almost seven years since I've seen you. That's how long Mario and I were in India. It seems like a dream.

"Before tomorrow's training course begins, you must tell

this seventy-eight-year-old woman all that has happened in your lives from 1940 to now. I want to know everything."

The laughter stopped. The two young women looked down at their hands.

"Even a year later, I can still see the destruction, the empty blocks, the holes where buildings should be," said Maria, scrubbing at a fork. "Half the children who were in the Montessori school at Laren were taken away to camps. No one escaped this great tragedy."

"No. No one," said Catherine. "My Geoffrey was so certain he would return. He said he had no fear. He couldn't wait to serve his country. He was killed in Operation Overlord while trying to rescue a wounded comrade. I have a medal in a drawer."

"My parents were killed on September 15, 1940, during the Blitz," said Elizabeth. "They were in their little garden behind our house in Deptford. They said they were not going to let a Luftwaffe pilot prevent them from weeding."

"A little girl from our school, Anne Frank, who died at Bergen-Belsen, is said to have written a diary that someone found and gave to her father. It will be published soon," Maria said. "I hear it is full of hope, despite every indication to the contrary. May God comfort you who have seen so much grief in your young lives."

There was a moment of silence as the three women sat before a tea tray. The fact of having tea at all seemed precious and miraculous. Catherine and Elizabeth watched as their beloved mentor made a paste out of soda and water. Dabbing some on the bowl of each spoon with a rag, she rubbed vigorously. Soon each spoon shone like a mirror.

"Now you must tell us something about your time in India," said Catherine.

Maria obliged. "I am much more interested in your lives, but I will tell you that I learned so much in India. I saw how closely attached mothers are to their infants. They take them everywhere; they aren't shut up in nurseries or lonely rooms or given to nannies to raise. Babies are everywhere in India. So I began to study them. I brought home one whole trunk filled with notes and observations.

"I wrote a book about infancy to age three. Mario and I also worked on a book called *To Educate the Human Potential.* I suppose the title tells you all you need to know about the content," said Maria, laughing.

"Do you still work every day from seven o'clock in the morning until eleven o'clock at night without stopping?" asked Elizabeth.

Maria leaned toward her with a conspiratorial whisper. "I tell them I am resting from one until three every afternoon, but that is actually when I go over my notes and write. It's our secret, right?" she said with a wink.

"How are your grandchildren?" Catherine wanted to know. "They must be grown up by now."

"They spent the war in Laren, under the care of their mother and the Pierson family. It was wrenching for Mario and for me to be separated from them. But they understood, as they saw classmates being taken away and parents of other students being wounded and killed in the war, that they were among the fortunate ones.

"Nothing stops children from growing, from changing. Not war, nothing. They will always keep seeking the light, no matter the circumstance. So it is with my own grandchildren. We left them as children. Now they are young adults, with the many interests, hopes, and dreams that young people have.

"Marilene is a great reader. Mario Jr. is, like me, a nomad. He was part of the resistance. He smuggled ammunition, weapons and microfilm across the border during the war. He is so humble, he told us none of this. We only learned it when he was awarded a commemorative cross. He plans to study psychology at the University of Amsterdam. He is interested in Freud, and we have many lively discussions.

"Rolando wants to go to America to make his way there. And Renilde has vowed she will follow in the footsteps of her father and grandmother and work with Montessori.

"They are all self-directed, loving, whole human beings. Their lives have been far from perfect. But they seem to know who they are. They have shown that they want to contribute, to make the world a better place. And yes, they are all stubborn, just like me," Maria said with a broad smile.

"And Mario?" Elizabeth asked. "What of Mario?"

"I have saved the best for last," Maria said proudly. "Do you remember Ada Pierson, whose family took us in?"

The two women began to giggle. Catherine said, "We can already guess. The day they met, eight years ago in London, we could already see the sparks."

"I guess I taught you to be observant, as Montessori teachers, and you took it to heart," Maria said. "You miss nothing."

"You can be sure of that," said Elizabeth. "Beyond the sparks, we noticed the endless collegial conversations, the lingering in the twilight after everyone else had gone . . . all the signs that love was growing."

For a moment, Maria was brought back to a time fifty years earlier when her own heart had raced, when her soul had felt connected to another.

"You've gone away from us, Mammolina," said Catherine. "What are you thinking about?"

"I am thinking that although the world may change in a million different ways, the feeling of love will always be the same."

Maria finished teaching the London training course in December 1946. She traveled to Scotland, where she was made an honorary fellow at the Educational Institute of Scotland. During her acceptance speech, she stated that her country was a star that turns around the sun and is called Earth.

On January 4, 1947, admirers and colleagues from all over the world gathered in Amsterdam to celebrate the fortieth anniversary of the opening of the Casa dei Bambini. Although she rarely used notes, Maria climbed the narrow, winding staircase to her office at 61 Konigsweg to write her speech. The office had become her retreat, the place where she could reflect.

The flowered wallpaper and view of green trees outside her window were a respite. Mario, Ada, and her grandchildren had helped her gather photos of friends, family, and travels. They hung on the walls and sat on the credenza across from her desk. She loved looking at them.

Maria sat at her large oak desk filled with stacks of blue note cards for her next book, which was to be on cosmic education. There was a stack of letters requesting lectures. She looked outside at the plane tree. A light snow had begun to fall. She could hear the voices of well-wishers gathering downstairs. She decided to begin her speech with a quote from her friend, the Indian poet Rabindranath Tagore: "Once we dreamt that we were strangers. We woke up to find that we were dear to each other."

"It is 1951, and you have been nominated three times for a Nobel Peace Prize," Mario Montessori said. "It must be some kind of record. It makes me furious that you haven't yet won."

"Don't dwell on what can't be," said Maria. "Look to the future. I have already received countless honors including the Dutch Order of the Orange-Nassau. Besides, the real heroes are the brave parents who brought their children to the first Casa. The students in India who had to sell their worldly goods and defy their parents to come to teacher training. Anna Maccheroni, who has given her entire life to this work. And you. You, my dear son."

Her eyes filled with tears. "And here I am, beginning to cry and missing the most important part of the trip."

They were walking carefully along the same ridge of the hill in Ancona where Maria and Renilde had found three chrysalises nearly seventy-five years before. They had been invited back to Italy for the reopening of the Opera Montessori, the administrative arm of Montessori schools.

Maria moved slowly. She leaned on her son. When they reached the top of the hill, they gazed out at the azure sea.

Maria recalled the feeling of her mother's warm hands on her hair, and the safety of laying her head in her mother's lap. Her skirt caught on a small branch and Mario leaned down to free it. He brought up a chrysalis. It sat in the palm of his hand. He held it as they made their way back down the hill.

Mario and Maria went on to the Ninth International Montessori Congress in London in May. Maria never wavered from her daily schedule. But her movements were more measured and effortful now.

As she approached the podium, the audience of more than five hundred watched in awe. She was eighty-one years old. Her eyes as serene as ever, she looked out at an audience comprised of people from fifty-three different countries. They represented Buddhist, Muslim, Christian, Jewish, and Hindu religions. The diversity was astonishing. But they were unified in one thing; a genuine interest in children and a hope for a future of peace through education.

Maria began by saying, "Children are human beings to whom respect is due, superior to us by reason of their innocence, and of the greater possibilities of their future."

"I've caught you, mother. Finally. Red-handed. You are supposed to be resting," Mario scolded. It was a sunny May afternoon. Maria was seated in a garden in the North Coast town of Noordwijk aan Zee, where she and Mario were staying with friends. She liked to go there for short vacations, although she still worked every day from seven o'clock in the morning until eleven o'clock at night.

"The sixth of May 1952 will go down in history as the day I caught my mother working when she said she was napping," Mario said, chuckling.

"Work is necessary, my dear. It can be nothing less than a passion. A person can only be happy in accomplishment," she answered with a grin.

"And what are you working on today, Mother?" Mario asked, smiling in spite of himself.

"I am looking at maps of Africa and making plans for where to go when we visit there. We have received so many requests I don't want to leave anyone out. And yet . . . it is a very large continent."

"Do you think you have the stamina for Africa?"

"Are there children somewhere who need to find their potential, to be given the chance to learn and become more fully human and create the kind of world we can sustain? Then I will find the stamina. Their innocence and the respect I have for them will keep me going."

"You could finally write the notes for your lectures, and I could give the lectures on your behalf and do the traveling. What would you say to that?"

"Seeing the children and the teachers learn and grow is my life's blood. Are you trying to make me obsolete?" Maria laughed. "All right, I'll close my eyes. But just for a moment. There is still so much more to be done."

Maria Montessori leaned her head against the back of the wicker chair. Her eyes closed.

Mario gazed lovingly at his mother. A monarch butterfly appeared. It fluttered gracefully around Maria's head before flying away. Maria's head turned to one side.

Mario suddenly grew alarmed. He took his mother's hand. It was warm, but he knew that she was gone.

As he knelt down beside her, the map of Africa slid from her lap to the ground in front of him. He considered it. "As long as there are children who have potential, there is still so much work to be done."

About the Author

Kate Fuglei is an actress, singer, and writer. She created a one-woman show, *Rachel Calof*, based on the memoir of a Jewish homesteader, and has performed it around America. It won Best Musical at the 2015 United Solo Festival in New York City. Kate has appeared in more than forty roles in episodic television and film, and she was in the First National Broadway tour of *Spring Awakening*. Based in Los Angeles, she has played leading roles in regional theaters across the country, among them Arena Stage, the Public Theater in New York City, and the La Jolla Playhouse. Two of Kate's short stories appeared in *SisterWriterEaters*, a book of essays about motherhood and food. Her first novel, *Fermi's Gifts*, was published in 2018. For more information, visit katefuglei.com.

NOW AVAILABLE FROM THE MENTORIS PROJECT

America's Forgotten Founding Father
A Novel Based on the Life of Filippo Mazzei
by Rosanne Welch

A. P. Giannini—The People's Banker
by Francesca Valente

Building Heaven's Ceiling
A Novel Based on the Life of Filippo Brunelleschi
by Joe Cline

Christopher Columbus: His Life and Discoveries
by Mario Di Giovanni

The Faithful
A Novel Based on the Life of Giuseppe Verdi
by Collin Mitchell

Fermi's Gifts
A Novel Based on the Life of Enrico Fermi
by Kate Fuglei

God's Messenger
The Astounding Achievements of Mother Cabrini
A Novel Based on the Life of Mother Frances X. Cabrini
by Nicole Gregory

Grace Notes
A Novel Based on the Life of Henry Mancini
by Stacia Raymond

Harvesting the American Dream
A Novel Based on the Life of Ernest Gallo
by Karen Richardson

Humble Servant of Truth
A Novel Based on the Life of Thomas Aquinas
by Peggy O'Reilly

Leonardo's Secret
A Novel Based on the Life of Leonardo da Vinci
by Peter David Myers

Marconi and His Muses
A Novel Based on the Life of Guglielmo Marconi
by Pamela Winfrey

Saving the Republic
A Novel Based on the Life of Marcus Cicero
by Eric D. Martin

Soldier, Diplomat, Archaeologist
A Novel Based on the Bold Life of Louis Palma di Cesnola
by Peg A. Lamphier

COMING IN 2018 FROM THE MENTORIS PROJECT

A Novel Based on the Life of Angelo Dundee
A Novel Based on the Life of Judge John Sirica
A Novel Based on the Life of Niccolò Machiavelli
A Novel Based on the Life of Scipio Africanus

FUTURE TITLES FROM THE MENTORIS PROJECT

Cycles of Wealth
Fulfilling the Promise of California
A Novel Based on the Life of Alessandro Volta
A Novel Based on the Life of Amerigo Vespucci
A Novel Based on the Life of Andrea Doria
A Novel Based on the Life of Andrea Palladio
A Novel Based on the Life of Antonin Scalia
A Novel Based on the Life of Antonio Meucci
A Novel Based on the Life of Artemisia Gentileschi
A Novel Based on the Life of Buzzie Bavasi
A Novel Based on the Life of Cesare Becaria
A Novel Based on the Life of Explorer John Cabot
A Novel Based on the Life of Federico Fellini
A Novel Based on the Life of Frank Capra
A Novel Based on the Life of Galileo Galilei
A Novel Based on the Life of Giuseppe Garibaldi
A Novel Based on the Life of Guido d'Arezzo
A Novel Based on the Life of Harry Warren
A Novel Based on the Life of Laura Bassi
A Novel Based on the Life of Leonard Covello

A Novel Based on the Life of Leonardo Fibonacci
A Novel Based on the Life of Luca Pacioli
A Novel Based on the Life of Maria Gaetana Agnesi
A Novel Based on the Life of Mario Andretti
A Novel Based on the Life of Mario Cuomo
A Novel Based on the Life of Peter Rodino
A Novel Based on the Life of Pietro Belluschi
A Novel Based on the Life of Rita Levi-Montalcini
A Novel Based on the Life of Saint Augustine of Hippo
A Novel Based on the Life of Saint Francis of Assisi
A Novel Based on the Life of Vince Lombardi

For more information on these titles and
The Mentoris Project, please visit
www.mentorisproject.org.